From Sunflowers to Growth Patterns

Data Representation and Analysis

Frans van Galen
Koeno Gravemeijer
Catherine Twomey Fosnot
Jennifer Smith

New Perspectives on Learning, LLC
1194 Ocean Avenue
New London, CT 06320

ISBN-13: 978-1-7320437-8-7

Table of Contents

Unit Overview

The focus of this unit is the extension of the development of children's ideas about data representation and analysis. A previous CFLM unit (*All About Sharks*) provided children with multiple opportunities to represent data using pictographs, bars, and line plots and introduced the use of two marked dimensions (horizontal and vertical scales), including the scaling of the axes. Emphasis was placed on: 1) comparing relations between bars; 2) interpreting line plots to examine frequencies using discrete categories, whole numbers, and landmark fractions (halves and fourths); and, 3) examining data by analyzing its shape when graphed.

This unit extends that work, including again the use of scaled axes on marked dimensions (horizontal and vertical scales), but also extending the markings on the scales to eighths. It also develops an understanding of range and builds a foundation for an analysis of central tendencies (mode and median), which will be more formally taught in grades 5 and 6. The unit is designed to align with the CCSS Standards of Mathematical Practice and the following core objective:

Measurement and Data 4.MD: Represent and interpret data.

CCSS.Math.Content.4.MD.B.4

Make a line plot to display a data set of measurements in fractions of a unit (1/2, 1/4, 1/8). Solve problems involving addition and subtraction of fractions by using information presented in line plots. *For example, from a line plot find and interpret the difference in length between the longest and shortest specimens in an insect collection.*

The Mathematical Landscape

From Sunflowers to Growth Patterns: Data Representation and Analysis is designed to extend children's emerging ideas and strategies regarding data representation and analysis. There are many ways to represent data and visually communicate relationships, and different models have different assets and limitations. Each model allows us to see different things and to ask different questions. However, just showing a graph does not mean children are able to "see" the mathematics in it. The mathematics is not in the model to be seen; it is in the child's mind. For this reason, as we work to develop children's understanding of data and representation we go back and forth: 1) from the mathematics to its representation; and, 2) from the representation and the questions that arise given the shape of the data to the mathematics. The tools used initially as models *of* thinking, become models *for* thinking.

Central to the sequence of units in this strand is the fostering of the ability to transpose data, meaningfully, onto a two-dimensional representation in a plane. We may broadly discern three types of data:

- ❖ categories; such as cats, dogs, or, blue, green, etc.
- ❖ measures; such as length, temperature, time, price, etc.
- ❖ frequencies.

Researchers often characterize the first two types in terms of *levels of measurement.* The first, concerning categories, is denoted a *nominal scale.* The second, concerning measures, can be structured in three different ways: using an *ordinal scale* (when values for a variable are progressively ordered; for instance, "strongly disagree," "disagree," etc.); using an *interval scale* (a scale which has equal intervals but for which zero represents simply an additional point of measurement; for instance temperature in degrees Celsius); and using a *ratio scale* (a scale which is proportional to the quantities being measured, including the value of zero; the key idea here is that the distance between the origin and a point on an axis signifies the corresponding measurement value).

Frequencies form a different type of data in that they are the result of counting the number of cases within a given category, or of a given measurement value. Frequencies especially come to the fore in two-dimensional representations, where one of the axes is one of the previously-mentioned measurement scales, and the other the frequencies. These will eventually develop into a means of getting a handle on a distribution of data on one variable.

Other types of two-dimensional graphs may consist of some combination of categories on one axis and measures of quantities on the other, or of measures on both axes. Graphs with two ordinal or ratio scales will eventually develop in later grades into a means of visualizing co-variation between two variables. This results in three types of two-dimensional graphs:

- ❖ value-bar graphs, which consist of a series of value bars adjacent to each other, but which can also be seen as two-dimensional graphs with categories on one axis (such as gardening zones) and measured quantities on the other (such as the number of days);

- ❖ frequency graphs, where one of the axes shows categories or measures, and the other frequencies;

- ❖ co-variation graphs, which have measures on both axes—each point of the graph combines two measurement values, (such as vertical growth and time), which correspond with the point's position in relation to the two axes.

These classifications and labels are used by researchers and are not important for your students to know at this point in their development, but they may be helpful information for *you* to know as you use this unit. This knowledge may provide you with a helpful lens for characterizing both the horizontal and vertical mathematizing—represented as pathways on the landscape—that you and your students will be travelling.

As you work with this unit and various types of data, you will also witness a complex network of relations emerging as your children grapple to understand and construct ways to analyze and represent data. We call this network a "landscape of learning" and characterize its landmarks as big ideas, strategies, and models. The landscape you will likely see developing as you work with this unit is shown below and a description of each landmark follows. The fuller landscape for data and representation in the elementary years is also depicted on page 10. The purpose of the graphic is to allow you to see the longer journey of students' development and to place your work with this unit within the scope of this long-term development. You may also find the graphic helpful as a way to record the progress of individual students. Each landmark can be shaded in as you find evidence in a student's work and in what the student says—evidence that a landmark strategy, big idea, or way of modeling has been constructed. Or, you may prefer to use our web-based app (www.NewPerspectivesOnAssessment.com) and add copies of student work as evidence to document your children's growth digitally. In a very real sense, you will be recording the individual pathways your students take as they develop as young mathematicians.

The Landscape of Learning

BIG IDEAS
❖ Intervals and frequencies can be unitized and scaled using ratios
❖ Frequency graphs can be used to compare data sets
❖ Frequency graphs can be translated into value-bar graphs, and vice-versa
❖ Two dimensions can show relationships between two physical quantities
❖ Adding the point (0,0) to both scales is necessary to see co-variation
❖ When depicting co-variation, inferences can be made about rate-of-change and measurement values between two data points
❖ Graphic representations can be used as tools for predictions

STRATEGIES
❖ Uses two axes but skips intervals
❖ Uses zero as a measurement on an interval scale
❖ Decomposes intervals into smaller units
❖ Scales intervals using ratios
❖ Uses two ratio scales to plot co-varying quantities
❖ Uses line graph with continuous data
❖ Interprets points between intervals on a line graph

MODELS
❖ Value Bars
❖ Line Plots
❖ Line Graphs
❖ Double Number Line

As students explore the investigations within this unit, several big ideas will likely arise. These include:

❖ *Intervals and frequencies can be unitized and scaled using ratios*
❖ *Frequency graphs can be used to compare data sets*
❖ *Frequency graphs can be translated into value-bar graphs, and vice-versa*
❖ *Two dimensions can show relationships between two physical quantities*
❖ *Adding the point (0,0) to both scales is necessary to see co-variation*
❖ *When depicting co-variation, inferences can be made about rate-of-change and measurement values between two data points*
❖ *Graphic representations can be used as tools for predictions*

❖ *Intervals and frequencies can be unitized and scaled using ratios*

With big numbers, interval scales create disequilibrium. There is no room on the paper to show the complete scale. What a constraint! This dilemma creates the need for a new construction—the intervals will need to represent more than just ones; they will need to be regrouped, unitized, and scaled using ratios. One interval can be used to represent 5 frequencies, or 10, or 100! What a big idea! But, using each interval to represent a consistent amount is important, otherwise the graph will not show the relationships proportionally.

❖ *Frequency graphs can be used to compare data sets*

Frequency graphs can become a powerful tool for comparing data sets. Here the shape of the graph may become the focus of attention. For example, students reasoning about the frequencies of different heights of beans across two lighting conditions can analyze the effect of light on growth.

❖ *Frequency graphs can be translated into value bar graphs, and vice-versa*

Data can be displayed in many ways. It can be displayed on a table and then transposed on a line plot to show frequencies. Bar graphs can be made from line plots and vice-versa. As students work with various graphs, transposing data from one form to another, they are building a strong foundation for analysis. Each type of graph has assets and limitations in displaying the data. In this unit, students come to see the value of bar graphs and line plots to show scaled data and even fractions of intervals, represented between the marked intervals.

❖ *Two dimensions can show relationships between two physical quantities*

Once scaling has evolved to represent proportional relationships between physical quantities consistently, the idea of using interval or ratio scales on both axes appears on the horizon. This is a huge insight and it opens the door to the development of Cartesian graphs. The need for proportional scales may be evoked by a task that involves change over time, for example representing the growth of a sunflower over time. Here the height of the sunflower may be depicted on a ratio scale, where time is shown on an interval scale. It's important to be consistent with the intervals placed on the new scale, though. If you leave some intervals out, the proportional relationships disappear!

❖ *Adding the point (0,0) to both scales is necessary to see co-variation*

As children work to coordinate their two scales proportionally, one of the new dilemmas they meet early on is what to do with the zero. The problem is that both scales have zeroes. Zero will need to be considered as a point because the zeroes on the two scales need to intersect, or the proportionality is compromised. Enjoy the disequilibrium you will see as students work to reconcile this issue! Cognitive reordering will certainly be required!

❖ *When depicting co-variation, inferences can be made about rate of change and measurement values between two data points*

Using two dimensions produces graphs that allow for reasoning about change in one variable (magnitude) in relation to another. This involves a shift from seeing isolated points on a Cartesian graph as pairs of two measures to interpreting the graph as depicting the co-variation of two variables. Some set of changes will form straight lines, but other patterns can appear, too. Consider for a minute how some variables are changing constantly (for example, growth over time). Interesting non-linear patterns of change begin to appear on the graph because growth over time is not always linear. (Imagine the growth of the sunflower over time. It goes through growth spurts and then stabilizes towards the end of its life cycle. The growth of humans is no different.) This new insight that graphs can depict co-variation not only allows data to be represented dynamically, it brings the graphic model into a new realm. It is becoming a tool *for* thinking, in contrast to just a representation *of* thinking. Inferences can be made about measurement values in between two data points and the door is now opened for analysis of the mathematics of change. Data points in a graph may be connected with a line segment, and a point on that line may be considered as an indication of what the actual measurement value might be. The steepness of the line segment in question may be discussed as a crude indicator of the rate of change.

❖ *Distributions of data can be characterized statistically*

Once children begin to see graphs as tools *for* thinking, they start analyzing the shape of the data distribution and they figure out ways to characterize what they are noticing. For example, they notice central tendencies, outliers, clusters, spread, and skewedness. They attempt to describe what they are noticing statistically with ideas such as the median and mode. In the long run, reasoning with statistics will develop into a form of reasoning that does not require graphs anymore. This unit lays the foundation for a beginning, emergent sense of statistics. But, developing a formal approach to calculating the mean and other statistical measurements is not within the scope of this unit.

As you work with the activities in this unit, you will notice that students will use many strategies to solve the problems that are posed to them. Here are some strategies to notice:

- ❖ *Uses two axes but skips intervals*
- ❖ *Uses zero as a measurement on an interval scale*
- ❖ *Decomposes intervals into smaller units*
- ❖ *Scales intervals using ratios*
- ❖ *Uses two ratio scales to plot co-varying quantities*
- ❖ *Uses line graph with continuous data*
- ❖ *Interprets points between intervals on a line graph*

❖ Uses two axes but skips intervals

As children begin to represent data using two scales, they initially often skip intervals and only represent the data they know. For example, when plotting the heights of the sunflower, they do not take data from missing intervals into consideration. They only plot the intervals they have data for. Although this strategy is to be celebrated when first used because it attempts to employ two dimensions using intervals, because some intervals are skipped the data shown is not proportional because some intervals are skipped. This makes growth patterns unobservable and also makes outliers much harder to identify.

❖ Uses zero as a measurement on a scale

Zero is added to a scale to represent a measurement. At this point though, zero is usually only placed on one scale. And when on two, the zeroes usually are not seen as an intersecting point of origin—a point represented as (0,0)—and the axes do not always intersect either.

❖ Decomposes intervals into smaller units

When data points fall on a scale between two marked lines, a dilemma of where to place the data occurs causing children to decompose intervals into smaller fractional portions.

❖ Scales intervals using ratios

Large values create an opposite problem where the length of the axis would need to be too long to fit on the paper. The solution usually is an attempt to scale the interval using ratios; each interval for example might stand for 5, 10, or 50.

❖ Uses two ratio scales to plot co-varying quantities

Finally, as children coordinate two measured quantities they come to realize that the scales on both axes need to be proportionally related to represent the data in a way that is useful for reflecting relationships between the two scales. When they plot points, they no longer skip missing data points, but they may still be challenged with how to align the scales proportionally. Both scales are now proportionally related, and the points of origin intersect. (0,0) is reflected on both scales at the intersection of the axes.

❖ *Uses line graph with continuous data*

Sometimes variables are continuous (like time, or length). When this is the case, a line graph can be used to represent the relationship that continues between data points.

❖ *Interprets points on a line graph between intervals*

Sometimes children will overuse a line graph model and the representation will not make any sense. For example, if they have discrete categories on the x-axis with frequencies plotted on the y-axis and then draw a line through the points, the graph makes no sense—the lines between the intervals cannot be interpreted. Similarly, if some intervals are missing the line does not show patterns of change over time—it is always a straight line! However, with two measurement scales showing all intervals, the line graph shows how the variables co-vary and the steepness between the points on the line show the pattern of change. Growth spurts can be seen and the points between plotted intervals can be interpolated!

MATHEMATICAL MODELING

❖ *Model of a situation*

Initially models emerge as a representation *of* a situation; later they are used by teachers to represent children's strategies. Ultimately, they are appropriated by children as powerful tools *for* thinking (Gravemeijer 1999). In this unit children engage in representing information about various situations onto graphs of various types. They use **Value Bars** for comparisons and **Line Plots** for frequencies, and eventually work with two scales to represent growth patterns, eventually transposing them into **Line Graphs**. As they work to represent their data in meaningful ways using these models, they modify their graphs accordingly, constructing ways to represent fractional amounts of an interval and even scaled data.

❖ *Model of Student Strategies*

In this unit, the **Double Number Line** and **Value Bars** are also used in minilessons to represent children's strategies as they work to determine where on the line (or bars) numbers would go. Representations like these provide a chance to see numbers as distances with their magnitudes transparently represented in relation to others. With the double number line, fractions are represented above with whole numbers represented below.

❖ *Models as Tools for Thinking*

Eventually children become able to use the open number line as a tool for thinking about scales for measurement and data representation. They are able to imagine the number lines as marked scales and understand how the position of numbers on a scale can be coordinated with a second scale to allow values and frequencies to be read at the point on the scale. But most importantly, as your children become able to represent data from situations competently, the graphic models themselves become powerful tools for thinking. Students notice the shape of the data and what it might mean. They talk about steepness and narrowness of clusters and central tendencies. They come to understand outliers and possible reasons for them. The models will in fact become not just representations *of* data, but tools *for* thinking.

References and Resources

Gravemeijer, Koeno (1999). How emergent models may foster the constitution of formal mathematics. *Mathematical Thinking and Learning 1* (2): 155–77.

DATA REPRESENTATION AND DATA ANALYSIS

Uses graphic representations for predictions of change

Graphic representations can be used as tools for predictions

Means can be found with division

Interprets points between intervals on a line graph

Uses line graph with continuous data

Distributions of data can be characterized statistically

Structures distributions using measures of central tendency

When depicting co-variation, inferences can be made about rate-of-change and measurement values between data points

Frequency graphs can be translated into value bar graphs and vice-versa

Adding the point (0, 0) to both scales is necessary to see co-variation

Uses two ratio scales to plot co-varying quantities

Scales intervals using ratios

Coordinates signify values of corresponding variables

Coordinate Plane

Decomposes intervals into smaller units

Two dimensions can show relationships between two physical quantities

Uses 0 as a measurement on a scale

Intervals and frequencies can be unitized and scaled using ratios

Frequency graphs can be used to compare data sets

Analyzes shape of data

Uses two axes but skips intervals

Plots frequencies using one-to-one alignment

Draws parallel lines to make it easier to "read off" frequencies

Places measurements on a scale parallel to the value bars

Line Plots

Two dimensions can show frequencies

Uses numerical relations to create proportional value bars

A second dimension can be used to quantify relations

Measures each value bar separately

Value Bars

Transitivity

Ratio-preserving mapping

Value bars can show relations

Number line

Comparative variations and seriation

Relations can be mapped and preserved

Uses mutually exclusive categories on a nominal scale

Compares objects by describing physical attributes relationally

Objects can be sorted by attributes

Sorts using attributes, but not with mutually exclusive categories

Categories should be mutually exclusive

The landscape of learning: data representation and data analysis on the horizon showing landmark strategies (rectangles), big ideas (ovals), and models (triangles).

DAY ONE

THE SUNFLOWER

Materials Needed

A Sunflower Picture (Appendix A)

Meter stick showing centimeters

Sunflower Growth Data (Appendix B, one per pair of students)

Several sheets of graph paper for each pair of students

Chart-size graph paper and markers for each pair of students

Pencils

Math Journals

Today students learn of a large sunflower that appeared almost magically in a city garden plot. Everyone involved in tending the garden said they hadn't planted it and so eventually it was assumed that a seed must have been dropped by a bird or brought to the plot by a squirrel. The context of the sunflower is used to introduce a set of data on growth over time. Working in pairs, students make graphs and use them to discuss the growth pattern of the sunflower.

Day One Outline

Developing the Context

❖ Show Appendix A and describe how a large sunflower grew in a city garden plot and everyone said they hadn't planted it! The person in charge of tending the plot had measured the sunflower and was fascinated by its growth.

❖ Present students with the known data on Appendix B and ask them to work in pairs to make a picture, graph, or display to show the growth.

Supporting the Investigation

❖ As students work, move around and confer. Support them to make displays, analyze the data, and consider the growth pattern of the sunflower.

❖ Look for moments to confer about issues such as whether the scales along the axes reflect the relationship between growth and time; whether a reader can tell the speed of growth from the graph; if missing data points matter; and whether bar graphs and line graphs show different things.

❖ Provide peer review in small groups, and then journal writing time for reflection.

Developing the Context

Use the picture in Appendix A to introduce the context about a large sunflower growing in a garden. The story may be told as a happening from your own life, as a story about a friend's garden, or as follows:

> In a section of the Washington Heights area of New York City, there is an abandoned lot that has been turned into a community garden space. Interested community members each sign up to take responsibility for a small space and then use it to plant flowers, fruits, and vegetables. They tend it, weeding and watering it throughout the growing season, and they each reap wonderful harvests each year—delighting in all the fresh, homegrown produce.
>
> One year, the strangest thing happened. A very large sunflower started to grow and no one claimed to have planted it! It just seemed to appear out of nowhere, and it was growing very fast! Everyone asked who had planted it and no one knew. Eventually they assumed that a bird flying over the garden had dropped a seed, or that a squirrel or other small animal had brought seeds to the plot and one had taken root. At first it was just a small plant with very tiny leaves and no one knew it was a sunflower, but in just 4 weeks it was already 17 cm tall. [Use the meter stick to show the height of 17 cm.] The community decided to measure the growth of the sunflower every week and posted a chart. The next week it had grown a lot—it was already 36 cm, more than twice the height it had reached in the first 4 weeks! Most weeks after this, however, people got busy with their own plots and forgot to measure the sunflower. So, these were in the end, all the measurements they had on the chart:

Appendix B

Weeks of Growth	Length in cm
4	17
5	36
9	169
14	253
15	254

Display Appendix B and ask students what they notice. They will probably start computing differences—how much the sunflower grew between each measurement. Assure them that they can calculate the precise numbers later and focus conversation on where the sunflower grew a lot (between weeks 5 and 9, and also between weeks 9 and 14) and where it grew very little (between weeks 14 and 15 it only grew 1 cm). Students may conclude that the sunflower had then reached its final height, just like adults do not grow taller any more after a certain point.

Point out that it is clear that in some periods the sunflower grew a lot, and in other periods, like in the last week, it did not grow very much. Suggest that if we want to study the growth of the sunflower, it might help if we try to visualize the growth in some way, in a picture or in some sort of graph.

Ask students to work in pairs. What kind of picture or graph they make is entirely up to them, but they should make a poster that makes it clear for everyone how much or how little the sunflower grew in the periods between measurements. Send them off to work on a flat surface (such as tables, desks pushed together, or on the floor) with markers and sheets of graph paper and a larger sheet of gridded chart paper. Encourage students to draft their ideas on the smaller paper before making their display on the chart paper.

Teacher Note:

This exploratory activity will likely generate bar graphs and line graphs. But, it is only the starting point of a series of investigations over the course of the unit so don't be concerned if no one generates a line graph, or if the graphs don't look perfect! The issues discussed in conferrals and the math congress with depend on the graphs that the students construct, but these discussions do not have to lead to final conclusions at this point in the unit. Some questions that may arise include:

- ❖ Do the scales along the axes reflect the relationship between time and growth? If so, how?
- ❖ Can a reader tell the speed of growth from the graphs?
- ❖ How should one interpolate missing data points?
- ❖ What are the differences between bar graphs and line graphs?

As the unit progresses, these issues will continue to surface. Look for those moments and bring the questions forth for discussion whenever possible. Line graphs are purposefully not introduced by explanation and practice, as students need time to explore the underlying reasons for using line graphs for themselves.

Supporting the Investigation

Let students get settled and ensure that everyone understands the goal of the investigation, then move around and listen in on some conversations. Note how students are depicting the growth. Do you see any emerging graphs; are the heights ordered; are there missing intervals on their scales; do students think that missing intervals matter; how do they interpolate the points between measurements; and are the zero points coordinated on the axes? These questions are all related to the landscape described in the Overview.

Most students will likely draw a graph with two axes, one vertical and one horizontal, simply because you have provided graph paper and they have probably been exposed to graphs before. How they use the axes and what they depict may be quite different, though! The main issue you want to focus on in this activity is how the numbers for height and time are placed along these axes. You can anticipate the following approaches:

❖ Some students may not consider the axes as scales along a number line and may even reverse the direction of the numbers. See Figures 1 and 2.

❖ The scale along the axis allows one to make ratio comparisons. If the axis for height has equidistant marks, with the numbers in equal steps (e.g. 20, 40, 60 cm..., or 50, 100, 150 cm...), one can see in the graph when the flower is, for example, twice as tall as at another point. Similarly, if the time axis has all weeks from 0 to 15 at regular intervals, one can visually compare periods in terms of ratios (e.g. the distance on the axis for a period of 12 weeks is three times the distance for 4 weeks). See Figure 5.

❖ Most students will probably not show all intervals, however. Be prepared that many will label at least one of the scales along the axis with only the numbers on the chart, ordered but spaced evenly regardless of their size. Thus, their graphs will not represent ratio comparisons. Or, it may happen that students start by putting 10, 20, 30, 40 cm... at regular spots along the axis and then discover that there will not be enough room for all the numbers. Instead of starting all over, they may just add the new numbers in larger steps, e.g. 80, 120, 160, 200, 240, 280. With respect to the time axis students often write only the numbers of the weeks when the sunflower was measured. See Figure 4.

❖ Some students may even use only the numbers that are given in the table on both axes. They may make a time axis with five equidistant marks for the weeks, and write the numbers 4, 5, 9, 14 and 15 near these. They also may make a height axis with only the numbers 17, 36, 169, 253, 254, disregarding all the intervals between these points. See Figure 3.

❖ Most students will likely do bar graphs, but you may have a few that do line graphs. This gives you an opportunity as you confer (or tomorrow during the math congress), to question around how to interpolate the points *between* the days when measurements were taken. See Figure 5.

❖ A few students may consider whether it is important to represent a point (0,0) that coordinates the two axes at their intersection. Most 4th graders do not do this. It is a big idea on the landscape and it takes a lot of exploring with graphic representation to even consider why this is important! But be aware of this issue as you move around. Your students may surprise you! See Figure 5.

This unit was field tested in both the U.S. and The Netherlands and so on the next few pages you will see samples of student work in English and in Dutch.

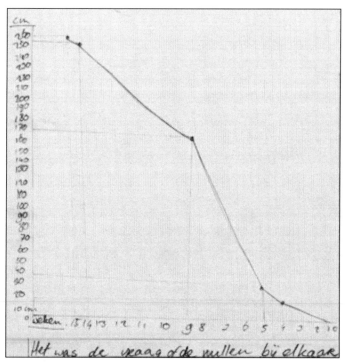

Figure 1. This work led to a discussion about whether it is important to stick to the usual order from left to right, or whether that is just a convention. The conclusion of the students was that indeed it probably is just a convention, but it is a handy one, as left to right matches with the way we write, read, and measure.

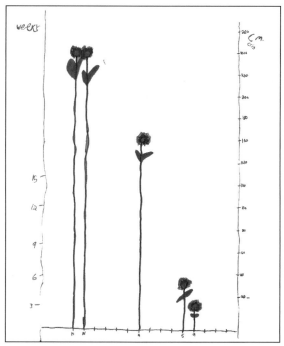

Figure 2. This graph is similar to the graph shown in Figure 1. These students started by writing the weeks near the vertical axis at the left, but then realized they wanted to put the length vertically and used the axis at the right for this. This probably caused the ordering of the weeks from right to left.

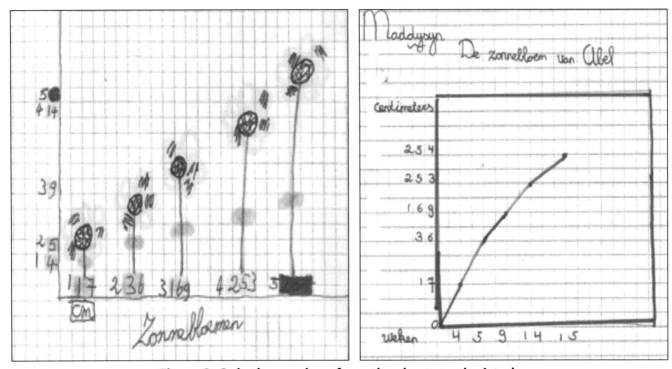

Figure 3. Only the numbers from the chart are depicted.
This results in a graph with a straight line through the data points.

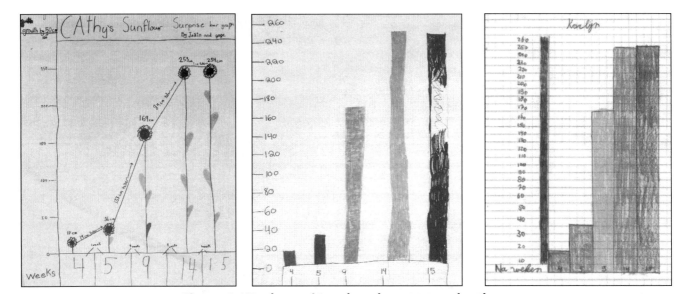

Figure 4. Weeks are just placed next to each other,
but the height axis includes all intervals and reflects the ratio relations.

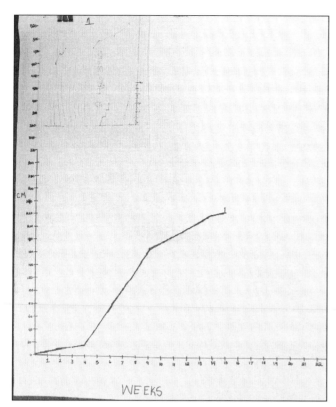

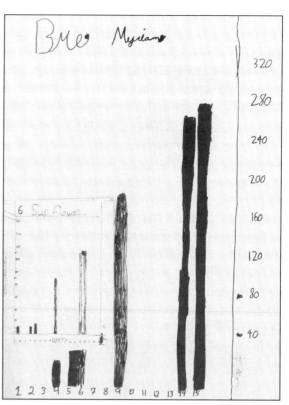

Figure 5. The axes for both time and height reflect all intervals and thus ratios but note how only the first sample uses a line graph and has the (0,0) point represented.

Inside One Classroom: Conferring with Students at Work

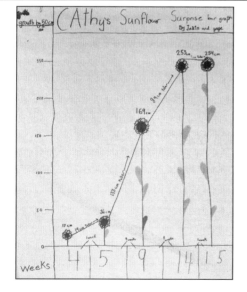

Jennifer (the teacher): What a nice graph you have here. May I sit and confer with you? I was listening to what you were saying about how to mark the measurements going up this line over here. You decided to mark 50, 100, 150, etc. Tell me more about why you chose those numbers.

Author's notes

As Jennifer moves around, she makes a point to listen in before sitting down to confer. And, note how her first move is about getting clarification.

Jaden: Sure. We knew we couldn't fit all the numbers from 1 to 254 on the line. So, we decided to just do these and then kind of estimate where our sunflowers should stop.

Jennifer: *(Smiling)* Good idea! It seems like you also went in order… every 50. You marked 50, 100, 150, 200, and 250. Was the order important to you?

Jaye: Well, we thought it would be helpful. Like a meter stick with marks to see how high the sunflower was.

Jennifer: That's a very interesting thing you considered! This line is like a measuring tool then, showing height. If you had switched at some point and made the numbers closer, like if you had put 200 much closer to the 100 would it have mattered?

Jaden: *(Puzzled at first, then intrigued)* Yeah. It would make it look like the sunflower hadn't grown very much! 200 cm is twice as high as 100 cm. We needed to show that. The sunflower really grew a lot from 5 weeks to here!

Jaye: Right! 100 cm in reality is a meter. So, 200 cm is twice as high. Yikes. Way up here! *(He jumps with his hand raised a bit to show how high.)*

Jennifer: I know. That is so important to show, and you figured out such a nice way to do that with your number choice and by showing the proportional relationships between numbers. I wonder if it might be important to show time like that, too? Do you think it might be important to think about this line across the same way you thought about your height line—as a measurement?

Jaye: But we labeled it here…

Jennifer: I know, and you did a nice job labeling it, too. But I was thinking about what you said about the height and how you wanted to show the distance between the points proportionally, so your readers could see the important difference in growth. When I look down here it looks as if 5 weeks and 9 weeks are right together. The sunflower grew this much in 4 weeks, this much in just 1 week later, but 9 weeks isn't just one week later than 5 weeks…

Jaden: It's 4 weeks later. I think we should do this part over, Jaye. We should show this like a timeline.

Jaden explains what she and her partner, Jaye, have done. They have developed a scaled model for the y-axis and connected it to a line of measurement, like a meter showing the centimeters.

Jennifer celebrates what the girls have done and draws attention to the markings in scale.

Next, Jennifer challenges the pair to consider missing intervals along the x-axis.

Conferrals do not always need to be long. Sometimes just listening carefully, offering a challenging question, and providing reflection time is all that is needed.

Once the work is well underway and students appear to be ready with drafts of their graphs, consider which partnerships would benefit from a critique from another group, and begin forming groups of fours for a peer review. In contrast to gallery walks, where posters are displayed publicly to the full community, peer review and critique with just another pair provides a safer, smaller group for discussion on just two pieces of work. The groups are more intimate, and the discussion can be deeper and more helpful. Pair different displays as you form groups. This will likely foster more discussion than if the two groups have done the same thing. Different approaches and insights can foster a bit of cognitive reorganization. For example, you might consider forming a group with displays like the ones shown in Figures 1 and 2 and having them discuss their representations with a group that has represented the data like the work shown in Figure 5. Or you might have groups form to discuss samples like those in Figure 3, where neither scale shows all intervals, and Figure 4, where the height scale shows all intervals. Discussions like these provide cross-fertilization and might even cause disequilibrium—a powerful way to support cognitive reordering!

As your students critique each other in small groups, move around and monitor the conversations. Ensure that conversations are positive and helpful, not hurtful or sarcastic. If this is the first time you have done peer critiques, you may find that you need to model, or fishbowl, a few. The important thing is to develop a risk-free environment and a seriousness about the work. A helpful resource on how to develop a classroom culture for this work is Ron Berger's 2003 book, *An Ethic of Excellence: Building a Culture of Craftmanship with Students.*

At the end of the peer review time, ask students to make entries in their math journals about the comments offered in their critiques and discussions and the resulting insights they had about displaying data to readers.

Reflections on the Day

Today students explored how data can be represented and analyzed to explore growth patterns over time. Several issues have likely emerged that will make for a lively and interesting math congress tomorrow, for example: 1) whether the graph reflects the relationship between growth and time; 2) can a reader tell the speed of growth from the graph; 3) do missing data points and intervals matter; 4) can a reader tell anything about the height of the sunflower on dates in time between the days the measurements were taken; and, 5) do bar graphs and line graphs show different things?

Data representation is an important abstraction and detachment from the original objects. It is a form of mathematizing the "lived world" and it introduces students to data analysis as a tool for predictions. It also lays the foundation for studying how values can co-vary, for example how variables like size can vary with time.

No matter where each student is on the landscape, they all had opportunities to come at the problem from different directions. And, as they worked to compare displays, several big ideas from the landscape have probably emerged: missing intervals matter, data can be plotted and displayed to show patterns of growth, and data representation can be a tool for predictions. Tomorrow your students will have an opportunity to transpose and/or revise their graphs as they prepare for a gallery walk and math congress. Many of the conversations that occurred in small groups today will likely resurface tomorrow in the congress.

DAY TWO

DISCUSSING GROWTH PATTERNS

Materials Needed

Meter stick

Whiteboards or small slates for the minilesson

Students' work from Day One and extra drawing paper if needed

Extra copies of Appendix B to use as needed

Markers

Sticky notes

Pencils

Math Journals

Today begins with a minilesson using the open number line, designed to support students to use proportional relationships to think about missing intervals on a measurement scale. Then students look over their journal entries from the day before and make posters for a gallery walk and math congress.

Day Two Outline

Minilesson

❖ Using a meter stick, draw a line from 0 to 100 cm.
❖ Working one at a time with a string of related points, ask children to close their eyes as you mark a point on the line. Then ask students what number might be there.
❖ After discussion on students' justifications for the numbers chosen, use the meter stick to show the correct number of centimeters and mark the related fraction of a meter so students can see how close they came.

Supporting the Investigation

❖ Move around and confer as students work on their posters.
❖ If revisions occur, ask students why, to understand the new insights they may have had since yesterday.

Facilitating the Math Congress

❖ Provide time for a brief gallery walk and then convene a math congress, inviting three or four pairs to lead the discussion of their graphs and conclusions about the growth pattern of the sunflower.

Minilesson: What number might this be?

Using a meter stick, draw a 1-meter line on the board. Explain that you used a meter stick and remind students that there are 100 cm in a meter. Mark the 0 and 100 cm points as you do this. Then, explain further that this minilesson is played like a game and that you are going to ask them to close their eyes while you make a mark on the line. When they open their eyes, they will write down the number they think it might be on their small whiteboards (or paper). With students' eyes closed, mark the first location, then start a discussion where children can explain their thinking about the number. Afterwards, show with the meter stick what number the mark really represents and write it under the mark so that students can see how close they came. Ask students what fraction of a meter that is and mark that, too, just above the line. As you go on with the minilesson, make sure all the earlier marks remain visible. The centimeters should be under the line and the fractional portions of the meter above the line.

The String:

50 cm

25 cm

75 cm

12½ cm

62½ cm

87½ cm

Behind the Numbers

The numbers have been chosen carefully to support children to think about number relations and landmark fractions. With the first mark, many children will likely guess 50 as they will see that you have marked a point halfway between 0 and 100. With the second mark, many will use ½ of 50, knowing that is 25. A few may try to divide the line mentally into 4 pieces and say 25, knowing that there are 4 quarters in a dollar. Some may just randomly guess, but you will get a sense of their understanding of magnitude from their guesses. Once the meter stick shows the first two marks, students have important information that can be helpful as the string goes on. The next number can be found by adding 50 and 25 and the remainder can be found by making use of 12½--which is half of 25. In this minilesson, the focus should be on the use of distances between the numbers, the proportional relationships, and the student justifications that are given.

Inside One Classroom: A Portion of the Minilesson

Jennifer (the teacher): I'm going to draw a line that is exactly 1 meter long. Here's the starting point, so I'll mark that 0, and here is the end so I'll mark that 100, because a meter has 100 centimeters in it. Today we are going to do a minilesson that is sort of like a game. I'm going to ask you to close your eyes while I make a mark and then you'll look and write on your whiteboard how far from 0 you think it is. Ok? Here we go. Close your eyes! *(She measures with meter stick, finds 50 cm. and marks the spot with a short vertical line.)* Ok, you can look! Write down the number you think might go here and hold your board up, so we can all see what you wrote.

Jennifer: Wow! I see so many 50s! Nicholas, why did you write 50?

Author's notes

Nicholas: Well, I guessed, but it looked about halfway, and I knew that 50+50 was 100.

Jennifer: *(Noticing that several children are nodding in agreement)* Who else guessed like Nicholas? *(Several hands go up.)* Ok, let's check *(laying the meter stick alongside the line and reading the centimeters).* Yep, a good guess, Nicholas. Exactly 50! I'll mark ½ directly above the 50, too, because it is ½ of a meter. Ok, here is the next one. Close your eyes. *(She makes a mark at 25 cm.)*

Jacob: It could be 25, because it is halfway between the 0 and the 50 marks.

Jennifer: Do people agree with Jacob? *(All hands show agreement.)* Nice reasoning. Let's check. *(She lays the meter stick alongside and marks 25.)* So what fraction should I write? Turn and talk to your elbow partner about this.

Gabe: *(Talking to his partner, Michelle)* Maybe ¼? I think there will be 4 equal pieces because a mark could be made between 50 and 100, too.

Michelle: I think you are right. There are 4 quarters in a dollar.

Jennifer: Michelle, come tell us what you and Gabe were talking about. I even have a nice wooden pointer you can use.

Michelle: *(Pointing to the mark)* This spot is 25 because 50+50 is 100. So, 25 is ½ of the 50… about here… because 25+25 is 50. There are 4 quarters in a dollar, and a dollar is 100 cents.

Mary: Nice. Did anyone think about it in a different way?

Allen: I agree. You should write down ¼, because ½ of ½ is ¼.

Jennifer: Oh, more nice thinking! It helps to use relationships we know, doesn't it? Ok, I'll write ¼. Let's go on to the next one. Close your eyes…

Notice how Jennifer introduces the minilesson by making clear what the 0 and 100 points stand for.

Note how Jennifer represents the numbers using a double number line. Centimeters are underneath the line and the fractions are along the top.

Jennifer continues bringing out the thinking of her students, all the while noting the number sense about fractions that they are using.

Supporting the investigation

Have students start their work today by reviewing their journal entries from the day before. It's always nice if you have had time to write to a few students about their reflections—either celebrating what they are thinking about or challenging them to consider some pitfalls (such as not showing all the intervals along both axes). Once students have had sufficient time with their journals, have them return to their partners to make a poster of their work. As students work, move around and confer. If you hear or see students discussing revisions, listen in to understand the insights they have had. These turning points can often be big moments to discuss in a subsequent congress.

Facilitating the Gallery Walk

Provide for a brief gallery walk where students can provide feedback to each other. Have them place their posters on display around the room and pass out lined sticky notes approximately 3" by 5" large. [Note: Using this size with older students suggests that their comments should be thoughtful, more extensive reviews than what can fit on smaller sticky notes.] Remind students that gallery walks should be quiet times so that all reviewers can read and think before commenting. Also remind students that it is better to only focus on one or two posters and write thoughtful comments than to do several superficial reviews that aren't particularly helpful to the authors. This time should be taken seriously. You might want to start with a discussion on the kinds of things that people might say that would be helpful to the authors of the posters.

During the gallery walk it's important that you make comments on posters as well. When you model the writing of helpful reviews, students will begin to do so also. Remember that it is important that students see you as a member of the community. And, as you move around, look for big ideas and strategies from the landscape. This is also a nice time to plan which pieces of work you will select for the congress.

Facilitating the Math Congress

Review the posters and choose a few that you can use to structure a discussion that will deepen understanding and support growth along the landscape of learning described in the Overview. There is not necessarily one best plan for a congress. There are many different plans that might all be supportive of development. You'll want this congress to foster development on the use of ratio scales, where each axis shows the intervals consistently, so the growth patterns of the sunflower can be discussed with meaning and a discussion can occur on how to interpolate the points between the known measurements. A window into one classroom follows as an example.

> **Tech Tip:**
>
> You might take pictures of students' work using an iPad and project them onto a whiteboard or smart board. When different ideas come up in discussions, revisions can be drawn without having to mark on the student's work. Apps such as *Adobe Sketch* or *Explain Everything* can be useful tools.

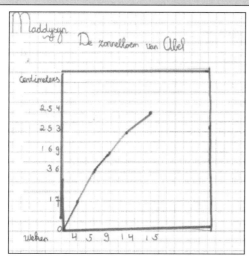

Author's notes

Jennifer (the teacher): Maddy, would you start us off and come talk about the graph you and Pierre made?

Jennifer chooses to start the congress with Maddy and Pierre's poster, where only the data from the table is shown. This move gets the question of missing intervals to the center of the discussion and prepares the way to discuss the importance of showing the intervals on both scales, the idea that Carter will share next.

Maddy: We put all the heights on this line, and then the weeks on this line going across. Then we found all the meeting places by going up and over.

Pierre: Then we connected the points with a line.

Jennifer: Yes, tell us why you connected the points with lines.

Maddy: *(She shrugs.)* You did that part, Pierre. Why did you do that?

Pierre: Because then they line up right and people can tell when they look at it that it makes a nice connecting line.

Jennifer: What do you think about what Pierre said. Is making a line important? What would the line show?

Carter: I like that you made points. I did that too, because at home I play Battleship and in the game you have to locate the ships with points. Then we made lines to connect the points on ours, too. But our lines look different. Your line is straight. Ours isn't.

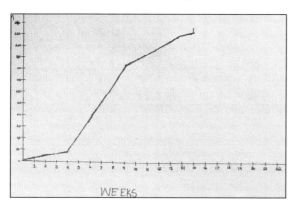

The discussion shifts towards comparing the two representations.

Jennifer: I know. I was going to have you share next because of that. Let's put your poster right here next to Maddy and Pierre's. Everybody, turn and tell your elbow partner what they did and talk about why the lines on these two posters look so different. *(After a few minutes of pair talk, Jennifer resumes whole group discussion.)* Ok, let's come back together and see if we can figure this out. Did anyone have a helpful partner? José?

José: Dominica helped me. She noticed that Carter has lots more numbers on his. Across the bottom you put weeks and you wrote 1, 2, 3... all the numbers. Going up you wrote the centimeters going 20, 40, 60... like that.

Jennifer: So, let's return to the question about why the connecting lines look so different.

José: I think maybe because Carter is showing what happened between the points?

Jennifer: What do you mean? Tell us more.

José: I think maybe the line is slanted because in the first 4 weeks the plant grew slowly, and then in the next week it grew faster. And then it shot up!

Jennifer: That's so interesting what you are saying José. So, if I put my finger here on this line what can you say about it?

José: I think that is maybe where the sunflower would be in 3 weeks... maybe around 12 or 13 centimeters?

Jennifer: So, let's discuss this question, do you think it matters if we don't put all the numbers evenly on our two scales... if we leave some out? Maddy?

Maddy: I think both are ok, it depends what you want to show. But the problem if you leave numbers out is that you can't tell how fast the sunflower grew. When you look at ours it seems like the growth was even, sort of like a little bit each day. But yours shows that it really grew fast here, between 5 and 9 weeks. It sprouted up! Maybe it got really good rain and sunshine then!

Pair talk is critical here as it is needed for reflection. Asking students to be a helpful partner also promotes the culture of the community.

The congress has been instrumental in supporting the community to consider how missing intervals can be a problem if one wants to examine the two measurement scales (in this case centimeters and time) as a relationship—growth as dependent on time.

Both representations are fine. But the first poster only shows what happened at a few selected discrete moments. The second poster interpolates the points between those moments and allows an examination of the growth patterns of the sunflower—a ratio of growth over time.

Reflections on the Day

Math workshop began today with a minilesson designed to support thinking about number relations, specifically fractions of a meter. Then as the students reviewed and revised their graphs from yesterday, they engaged in some revision work and had a gallery walk for more feedback. The congress was then used to provide discussion on a few of the big ideas on the landscape. It is helpful as you work through this unit to document for each child the growth you are seeing along the landscape. Make copies of the graphic in the overview or use our web-based app from www.NewPerspectivesOnAssessment.com. As you glean insights about how each student is thinking, highlight it on the graphic. Over time you will have a nice documentation of each student's learning pathway as they develop as young mathematicians.

DAY THREE

GROWTH PATTERNS OF BRASSICA RAPA PLANTS

Materials Needed

Four Student Graphs
(Appendix C, one per pair of students

Graph Paper for Brassica Rapa
(Appendix D, several copies per pair of students)

Focus Questions on Brassica Rapa
(Appendix E, one copy per pair of students)

Pencils

Math Journals

The day begins with the introduction of a fast-growing plant—Brassica Rapa—and a look at some graphs made by four 4th graders on the growth patterns of their plants. Students analyze some of the problems in the graphs, transpose the data onto better graphs, and then draw conclusions culminating in science reports based on their new graphs and subsequent peer critiques.

Day Three Outline

Developing the Context

❖ Introduce a fast-growing plant called Brassica Rapa.
❖ Display four student-made graphs from another 4th grade class showing the measurements taken on different days (Appendix C).
❖ Invite discussion on the graphs.
❖ Pass out focus questions (Appendix E) and graph paper for transposing the data (Appendix D) and have students work in pairs.

Supporting the Investigation

❖ Move around and confer as students transpose the data to make new graphs and discuss the focus questions.
❖ Have students work on science reports in their math journals using the graphs as evidence for their conclusions.
❖ In peer critique groups, have them discuss their conclusions.

Developing the Context

Explain that you have some data from another 4th grade class that did a project on growing plants. The students in the class each got their own little plant and made detailed observations about its growth. The plants were a variety of Brassica Rapa chosen because it grows very fast. If you put a seed in the soil, in can grow into a mature plant that will have seeds itself in just 40 days. As part of the project the students had to measure their plant regularly. Near the end of the project they made a graph of their data.

> **Teacher Note:**
>
> It is particularly nice as you progress through this unit to engage your students in growing their own plants, too. Wisconsin Fast Plants® (https://fastplants.org) specializes in seeds for schools to use. The company sells a variety of Brassica Rapa–a mustard green with yellow flowers that reaches maturity within 40 days. Searching for Wisconsin Fast Plants on the internet will also yield several video clips that you can use to develop the context.

Show Appendix C, which has the work of four children. Have students form small groups of three or four and provide each group with a paper copy, unless the projected display is large enough for all to see in detail. Ask students to study the graphs and discuss what they notice about each one. How are the graphs different? What did each student do? Provide five to ten minutes of small group discussion time and then start a whole group discussion on the graphs.

Appendix C – Four Student Graphs

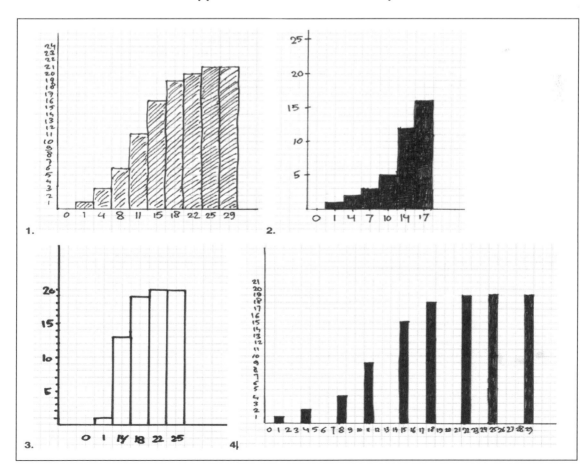

The following points will likely come up in the discussion:

❖ Not all students measured their plants on the same dates.
❖ In graphs #1, #2, and #3, the value bars are placed next to each other, but the student who did graph #4 left spaces for the days when measurements were not taken. [Note: if this point is brought up, ask students which approach they think is better and why.]
❖ In graph #4, sometimes there are two days between measurements and sometimes three; this is probably because a week has seven days and the students do not go to school on the weekend and so they cannot measure their plants on those days.
❖ The students who did graph #1 and graph #4 measured on the same days, but in graph #4 the days that the plant was not measured were represented but left open.
❖ The students who did graphs #2 and #3 measured their plants at irregular days.
❖ The student who did graph #2 probably stopped measuring before the plant had reached its full growth.
❖ The student who did graph #3 did most of the measurements later.

After a preliminary discussion on what students have noticed in the graphs, pass out Appendix D, Graph Paper for Brassica Rapa, explaining that if they want to redo the graphs they can.

Appendix D – Graph Paper for Brassica Rapa

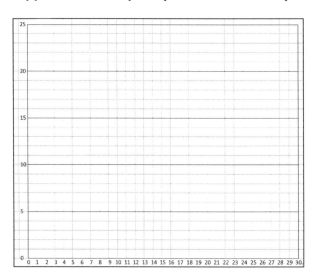

Ask that students work together in pairs to answer the questions on Appendix E.

Appendix E – Focus Questions on Brassica Rapa

❖ Are there differences in the growth patterns of the four plants?
❖ What can you tell in general about the growth of this kind of plant?
❖ About how high do the plants become?
❖ Do the plants all grow at the same speed all the time, or do they have growth spurts like the sunflower where they grow quickly?
❖ About how long does it take for a Brassica Rapa plant to reach its full height?

Supporting the Investigation

As the students work, move around and confer. Note if they redraw the first three graphs, transposing the data onto a blank graph to show all the intervals. If they don't, ask them if they think doing so would show anything new. Probe to see what they think about missing intervals and then suggest they transpose the data onto the blank graph to see if the intervals matter. If you see students combining all the data onto one blank graph, remind them that the data are from four different plants and ask how they will go about answering the first question if they combine everything.

Once students have had sufficient time examining the graphs and working with the focus questions, have them work individually in their math journals writing a science report on the growth of the Brassica Rapa plant using the data on their graphs as evidence. Then have students form peer review groups to share their findings and receive critiques on their reports. Move around and listen in on some of the discussions. Listen for arguments on how students know that the plant does not grow at the same speed all the time.

Teacher Note

Most students will probably find that the plants grew until they were about 20 cm high. Graph #2 suggests that the plant only grew to 16 cm, but the other graphs show that it takes longer than 17 days before the Brassica Rapa has reached its final height. There are differences between the four plants, with some growing slightly taller than others, but generally the growth patterns are similar, with the most rapid growth occurring between 8 weeks and 18 weeks. In the first days the plants grow slowly, then they grow more quickly, but then growth slows down again around day 20 and around day 22 the plants stop growing.

Reflections on the Day

Today was likely a turning point for many of your students in their ability to understand why it is important to include consistently spaced intervals on both scales—it helps the reader understand how two variables are related. Using two ratio scales (such as time and height measurements) allows one to see growth patterns over time. Without consistent and evenly-spaced intervals, growth can look like a straight line, when in fact there are times when the growth speeds up. Remember to document your students' learning on their landscapes. Tomorrow students will have an opportunity to explore and use a different kind of graph—a line plot—to study beans that have been grown in different conditions.

DAY FOUR

PLOTTING BEAN SIZES

Materials Needed

Yardstick (with ½, ¼, and ⅛ inches marked)

Small whiteboards and markers or paper

A small package of dried fava beans

Beans from Different Soil Conditions (Appendix F, for display)

Measurement Data on Beans from Different Soil Conditions (Appendix G, one copy per pair of students)

Graph Paper

Markers and Pencils

Math Journals

Today begins with another minilesson like the one used on Day Two: *What Number Might This Be?* Students are then introduced to a new investigation where they are presented with a variety of beans grown in different conditions. After measuring the resulting sizes of the beans, students make line plots of the data and analyze the effect of the various conditions on the frequency and size of the beans produced.

Day Four Outline

Minilesson: A String of Related Problems

❖ Using a yardstick, draw a line end-to-end and mark it 0 to 36, reminding students that a yard has 36 inches.

❖ Working one at a time with a string of related points, ask students to close their eyes as you mark a point on the line. Then ask what number might be there.

❖ After discussion on students' justifications for the numbers chosen, use the yardstick to show the correct number for each mark so students can see how close they came.

Developing the Context

❖ Explain that scientists determine the effect of growing conditions on plants by experimenting and collecting data.

❖ Show and discuss the experiment and the beans from two different soil conditions shown on Appendix F.

❖ Measure a few fava beans just to show students how the measurements were done and then provide Appendix G with the measurement data. Send students off in pairs to make a line plot for each sample to determine if the soil had an effect on the beans' size.

Supporting the Investigation

❖ Move around and confer as students work.

Minilesson: What Number Might This Be?

Draw a straight line on the board using a yardstick. Mark 0 at the beginning and 36 at the end. Remind students of how the yardstick has 36 inches and review how to play *What Number Might This Be?* [Directions can be found on Day Two of this unit if you need them.]

The String:

18
9
3
1
1/2
1/4
1/8
3/4
3/8

Behind the Numbers

As always, the numbers have been chosen carefully to support students to think about number relations. 18 is used first because it is the midpoint and will serve as a helper in locating other numbers as the string continues. 9 will also be easy as it is half of the 18. With 3 next, students may try to judge what the distance is and think about thirds, but there will be some room for error. Once the 3 is marked it will be easier to see that 1 is 1/3 of 3. The next four numbers are easy because they can be seen as halving the distance between two known points. 3/8 is half of the distance from 0 to 3/4 because the denominator has doubled and the numerator stayed the same, or because 3/4 = 6/8 and now the numerator has halved and the denominator stayed the same, but it is also the midpoint between 1/4 and 1/2 if students think about 1/4 as 2/8 and 1/2 as 4/8.

Developing the Context

If you do an internet search of *growing broad beans* you should find some nice time lapse video that shows the growth of the plant. Using video clips like this is a great way to get your students interested in the context. Once you have them intrigued, tell them that some students in the same class that grew the Brassica Rapa plants also did an experiment on the effect of soil conditions on bean plants. [If you are doing planting with your students while doing this unit you can engage a group in a similar experiment.] They varied the soil conditions and grew two fava (broad) bean plants, one in each condition. Both were grown in good compost soil, but one was given extra fertilizer. When the plants reached maturity, the students gathered all the pods of the two plants, carefully keeping them in separate piles (one that had been grown with a little extra fertilizer, and the other one that had not received fertilizer). They counted all the beans in each pile and measured them. Display Appendix F (Beans from Different Soil Conditions). The first image shows the beans of the plant without fertilizer; the second one shows the beans of the plant with fertilizer.

Appendix F – Beans from Different Soil Conditions

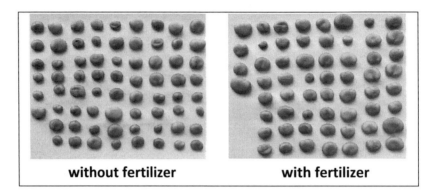

Ask your students to consider both sets of beans and talk for a few minutes with a partner about any differences they see. Students will probably remark that the plant with no fertilizer has produced more beans. They might also remark, however, that the beans from the plant with fertilizer seem to be a bit bigger. Ask if it is true that the beans of the plant with fertilizer are indeed larger than the other beans and how one might find out. Most students will suggest measuring the beans. Measure a few dried fava beans to show how the students who had done the experiment might have done so, but then provide Appendix G with the measurement data explaining that you don't have the exact beans grown in the two conditions, only the pictures, but you do know the measurements. Pair students and send them off to consider the data and think about what it shows.

Supporting the Investigation

Let students work for a bit in their groups. See if any suggest making line plots. Remind them that their task is to find a way to summarize the data and to draw conclusions. At some point you may suggest that they make line plots. The finished graphs should look like these:

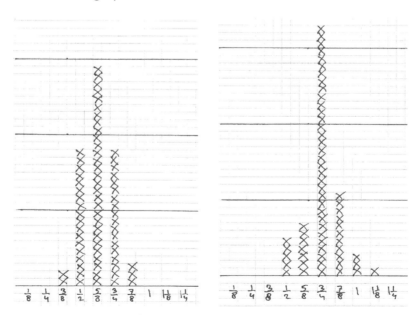

Figure 6. Line plots of beans grown without fertilizer (left) and with fertilizer (right).

As students work, note how they plot the fractions along the axis. Are they familiar with the fractions? Can they order them? This is a nice time to support students with an understanding of fractions as well. Remind them of the minilesson. Some may say the fractions should go on a line, like on the yardstick, not in the space between lines. Acknowledge that point. It is an astute observation. Point out though that in the making of a line plot the fractions are being thought of not just as a measurement, but also as a category and the purpose of making a line plot is to determine how many beans are in each category. So, either representation is fine.

> **Tech Tip:**
>
> You might take pictures of students' work using an iPad and project them onto a whiteboard or smart board. When different ideas come up in discussions, revisions can be drawn without having to mark on the student's work. Apps such as *Adobe Sketch* or *Explain Everything* can be useful tools.

Once students have their line plots made, ask them to discuss their conclusions about the experiment. Have them use their math journals to record their observations and conclusions and remind them to use the data in their justifications. As you confer, bring up questions like: how many beans were in each sample; what was the range of size in each sample; what does the spread look like; and are there clusters? Encourage students to use the shape of the data, as well as individual numbers, as a justification for conclusions. You might also ask if they think it matters that only two plants were used in the experiment.

Reflections on the Day

Math workshop began today with another minilesson designed to support the development of number relations—this time fractions of an inch. It may potentially also have supported some students to consider how to measure fractions of an inch and to depict them along the x-axis. As you moved around and conferred as students worked, you likely gained a deeper understanding of where each child is in understanding graphic representation. Take some of their journals home tonight and read through them to see where they are in their ability to analyze data. This is a great way to do formative assessment—much better than giving a test or doing a time-consuming interview. The journal is a nice place to dialogue with students individually, as well. Students will love getting and reading a personal note from you when they review their journals. Each day you should see your children making progress on the landscape, but each child's pathway will likely be different. The lessons are not designed with one goal for all—one "it" for everyone to get. Each child should be learning, but most likely they are not all learning the same thing. Learning *is* development. Remember to document the journey of each child on individual landscapes, too!

DAY FIVE

ANALYZING THE DATA

Materials Needed

Students' work from Day Four

Appendix F (extra copies if needed)

Appendix G (extra copies if needed)

Blank or graph style poster paper (one or two sheets per group of four students)

Markers and Pencils

Sticky notes (3" by 5" lined)

Math Journals

Today begins by asking students to read over their journal entries from the day before and to reflect on and justify their conclusions about the bean plant experiment. Students then form groups of four to discuss their findings with each other and make a poster for a gallery walk. Posters are then displayed around the room and a gallery walk ensues. A math congress is held afterwards with emphasis placed on using evidence from the graphs as a basis for conclusions.

Day Five Outline

Supporting the Investigation

❖ Ask students to read over their journal entries from the day before and to reflect on their conclusions and justifications.

❖ Form small groups of approximately four students each and have them share and discuss their conclusions.

❖ Ask students to make one poster per group listing their conclusions and emphasizing the importance of using data on the graphs as evidence for conclusions.

Facilitating the Math Congress

❖ To prepare for the math congress, have a brief gallery walk, inviting peer review.

❖ Provide time for revisions if desired.

❖ Choose two or three posters for discussion or bring up some of the main points listed on several posters for a deeper discussion.

❖ To conclude, provide five minutes of quiet reflection time for journal writing on the difference between the graphs constructed for the sunflower and the line plots used in the bean experiment.

Supporting the Investigation

Start math workshop today by allowing students to review their line plots and journal entries on their conclusions about the bean plant experiment. Then form small groups of approximately four students each and ask them to make a poster listing their conclusions and justifications using their line plots as evidence.

Facilitating the Math Congress

To prepare for the math congress, have a brief gallery walk, inviting peer review. Ask students to write thoughtful comments and remind them it is better to do a few comments thoughtfully than to do several superficially. Also remind them that a gallery walk is done in silence to allow everyone to think. Afterwards provide time for students to make revisions if desired and then convene a math congress. The structure of the congress depends on the posters of your students. If different posters have different analyses, then choose a few different ones that will provide new insights as they are discussed. On the other hand, if most of the posters have similar conclusions a share of two or three posters is not necessary. In fact, it would be redundant. It might be better to just pick out a few of the major points that students observed from the representations, such as the fact that the non-fertilized bean plant had more beans, but they were smaller. The data on the line plot of the fertilized plant shift more to the right and even extend to 1 1/8, with a mode and median of 3/4. The plot of the unfertilized plant is shaped like a bell curve with a mode and median of 5/8. End the congress with some quiet reflection journal writing time on the difference between the graphs students made to show the growth patterns of the sunflower and the line plots they made to examine the growth of the beans. How were the graphs different and what did each graph contribute?

Reflections on the Day

At this point you are halfway through the unit. Your students have worked with line plots, tables, and ratio scales. They have explored how important it is to show all the intervals on ratio scales in order to see patterns of growth, and they have explored how line plots can be used to examine frequencies, clusters, and ranges. Next week they will work further with bar graphs and the distribution of data and then later in the week they will explore line graphs. The small group peer reviews with time to revise supported students to take the work seriously and to share in a more risk-free environment than presenting in front of the whole class. Practices like these, along with your conferrals and reflective comments in their journals, implicitly tell your students that you take their ideas seriously. You see them as young mathematicians at work and trust them to learn. They know it and will rise to the occasion.

DAY SIX

GROWING CONDITIONS

Materials Needed

Lengths of Growing Seasons (Appendix H for display)

Data from Plant Experiment (Appendix I, for display and for each pair of students)

Data Reordered by Size (Appendix J, for display and for each pair of students)

Pencils

Math Journals

The day begins with another minilesson using number relations to find lengths, given the known lengths of others. But, with this activity you and the students will be making a bar graph of the lengths of various growing seasons around the world. After the minilesson, students are provided with data from an experiment on the effect of light on plant growth in two conditions: growing on the windowsill; and growing under a lamp that is on 24 hours a day. Students draw conclusions from the graphs they are given and develop justifications for their conclusions.

Day Six Outline

Minilesson

❖ Display Appendix H, asking students to tell you the length of the longest growing season. Shade the length in completely, marking it on a number line below as 365 days.

❖ Using 365 as a benchmark, invite students to tell you how far to shade in each of the 10 other bars and to justify their decision using number relations.

Developing the Context

❖ Show images of vegetables grown in Alaska with 24 hours of sunlight.

❖ Describe an experiment and display Appendix I showing the results.

❖ Provide discussion on the results and share Appendix J with the results reordered.

Supporting the Investigation

❖ As students work to analyze the data, move around and confer supporting them to consider the distribution and central tendencies of the data.

❖ Provide journal writing time.

Minilesson: Lengths of Growing Seasons around the World

This minilesson is somewhat like the minilessons in the prior week in that it invites students to consider number relations by finding lengths, given the known lengths of others. But, with this activity you and the students will be making a value bar graph of the lengths of various growing seasons around the world. There are 11 seasonal zones based on the average length of frost-free days.[1]

Project a copy of Appendix H onto a smartboard or whiteboard—or any surface you can draw on. Explain to students that you will be filling in bars to represent the lengths of the zones, but it will be important for them to think out strategies and provide good justifications for where a number goes because today you won't be using a meter or yard stick to check. The lengths of the bars are given in days. Explain to students that you will help them get started by doing the longest one. Ask them to look at the list and find the longest growing season (it is Zone 11: 365 frost-free days). Draw a number line below to the end of the bars, marking the end of the bars on the number line as 365 days (as shown in Figure 7). Then shade in the bar for Zone 11 to the end. Invite students to pick a zone to do next and to choose wisely, thinking about a good strategy to determine where to mark the related bar. Once the bars are all shaded and marked, invite conversation on how the bars are related. A dialogue box is provided to help you envision what the flow of the conversation might be like, and how the zone lengths might be marked and compared.

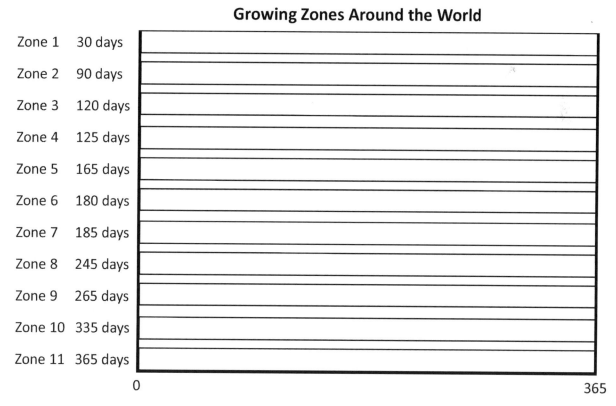

Growing Zones Around the World

Zone 1	30 days
Zone 2	90 days
Zone 3	120 days
Zone 4	125 days
Zone 5	165 days
Zone 6	180 days
Zone 7	185 days
Zone 8	245 days
Zone 9	265 days
Zone 10	335 days
Zone 11	365 days

0   365

Figure 7: Drawing an open number line under Appendix H.

---

[1] Data is from https://www.dummies.com/home-garden/gardening/growing-seasons-by-hardiness-zone/

Jennifer (the teacher): Now we know the marking of Zone 11. I'll shade the bar in. This length will be 365 days. Think about which zone you want to do next… and remember, pick one that you have a good strategy for. Its length will need to be scaled in relation to this mark to keep the numbers proportionally related. Show me with a "thumbs up" when you are ready.

Alena: I can do 2 of them. 180 and 185. Half the year is about 180 days… well… 182… and… ½. I knew 180 because that's how many days we are in school. (*She smiles.*) So, make a mark halfway and then put 180 just before it and 185 just after it.

Jennifer: Oh nice. Wow! I'll shade in the bars and mark the numbers on the number line. Who is ready with another?

Allen: I can do 90. It's half of 180. And I know it is halfway between 0 and 180, but also 4 x 90 = 360.

Irina: We can also do Zone 9. It's close to 270. I used Allen's idea. He said 4 x 90 = 360. Three parts would be 270 because 180 + 90 = 270.

Jennifer: (*Noticing that several children are nodding in agreement*) Are there any others that we can do?

Pierre: I have a good way to do 30. It is 1/3 of 90.

Michelle: I agree and now we can do 120 because that's 30 + 90.

Jennifer: Nice. Did anyone think about 120 in a different way?

Maia: I used 1/3 like Allen, but I did 1/3 of 360. 120 + 120 + 120 = 360.

Jennifer: Oh, interesting! So, Allen said 4 x 90 and then did 1/3 of 90 and got 30 and you did 1/3 of 360 and got 120. Let me shade these bars in. Ok, now let's look at them. How does Zone 3 compare to Zone 1? Here is an important question that I want you to discuss with your elbow partner. When you look at the graph and compare the zones, what relationships do you see? (*Jennifer provides a few minutes of discussion time and then resumes whole group discussion.*) Salena and Max, what did you discuss? Start us off.

Salena: Zone 3 is 4 times longer than Zone 1. And Zone 11 is about 4 times longer than Zone 2.

Author's notes

Notice how Jennifer urges students to jump around the list and consider relationships. Doing so encourages them to use number relations.

Jennifer continues bringing out the thinking of her students, all the while noting the number sense that they are using.

Developing the Context

Use the information in the box to the right as a way to introduce the context. The information will follow nicely from the minilesson. Students will love seeing the huge vegetables grown in Alaska that are shown on the National Geographic site. Then explain that the 4th graders, from the class that grew Brassica Rapa and did the bean experiments, tried to study the effect of light, too. Each of the 21 students had taken care of a plant and recorded its growth. The plants were placed on the windowsill, so they would get as much sunlight as possible. There were 10 plants left so the teacher made a box with room for the 10 extra plants, and placed a lamp over it, like the kind used in greenhouses, that would be left on for 24 hours. Now the class could do a nice experiment: would the 10 plants under the light grow better than the other plants?

Ask students to discuss what data should be collected in order to see if the plants in the box grow better. Provide a bit of discussion time and then share what the other class had decided.

They decided that the height of all plants would be measured on the same day—day 18. They thought that if plants actually grow better because of more light, then the plants under the lamp should be taller than the other plants on the windowsill. Explain that you have graphs of their results and display Appendix I. Ask students to look at the graphs and determine what the bars in the graphs stand for and then to discuss two questions:

❖ Did the plants under the lamp, with 24 hours of light, grow more than the other plants?

❖ If they did, how many inches more did they grow?

Teacher Note:

Alaska has a very short growing season as most of the state is in Zone 2. However, the Alaskan growing season does not have dark nights. The Arctic is tilted toward the sun during the growing season and the plants grow in almost 24 hours of sunlight. In a growing season that is months shorter than most, Alaska's gardeners grow some of the largest produce because of the sunlight: 75-pound cabbages, 100-pound kale and 1,000-pound pumpkins! For pictures go to:

https://www.nationalgeographic.org/encyclopedia/growing-season/

Appendix I – Data from Plant Experiment

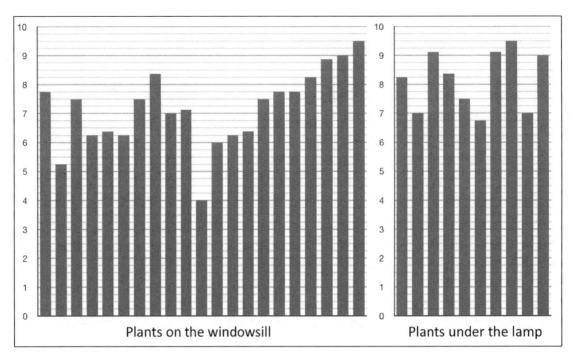

Let students discuss for a few minutes how they would proceed to answer the questions. After this ask them if they would rather have the data presented in another way. Most likely some students will say that the task would be easier if the bars were put in order of size. If this idea comes up, display Appendix J where the bars have been ordered by size. [Note: If students do not request or suggest a reordering, then suggest it.]

Appendix J – Data Reorded by Size

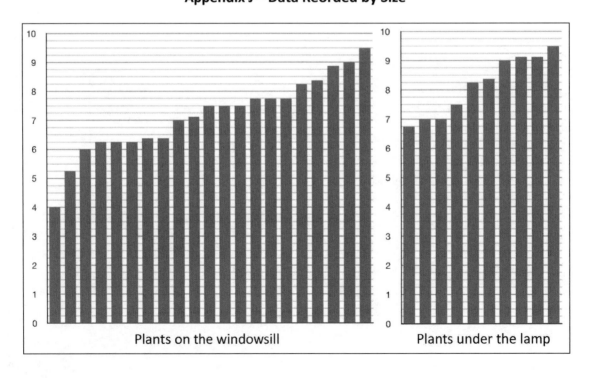

Supporting the Investigation

The main goal of this investigation is to discuss the idea of using "the numbers in the middle" as a way to compare the two distributions. It is not to teach the idea of the mean, or the procedure to find it. It is common that students will talk about "the average," but they will most likely not be referring to the arithmetic mean. First, because that concept is not usually introduced until grades 5 or 6 and, even if they do know how to find the average by adding and dividing, they probably do not have a good understanding about why the procedure works. Most likely they are referring more vaguely to numbers in the middle that are seen to be typical. This intuition leads nicely into examining the central tendency of the distribution in an informal way and the development of the median: the number that is exactly in the middle of the distribution.

As you move around to confer, you will likely see a variety of strategies. Some students will start by using a 1-1 correspondence strategy—comparing bars to bars. Even though one group has 21 plants and the other has only 10, they will likely note that the tallest windowsill plant is about the same as the tallest plant under the lamp. They will also likely note that the shortest plants in each group are quite different and the shortest plant is in the windowsill group, with a difference of 2½ inches. They may also compare the midpoint bars. This is a nice place to define median if it emerges naturally. The median of the windowsill group (plant #11) is about 7½ inches; whereas the two "middle plants" (#5 and #6) in the plants under the lamp are about 8¼ inches. To find the difference in the growth of the plants students may find the difference between these two numbers and offer ¾ of an inch as an answer to the second question. See Figure 8a.

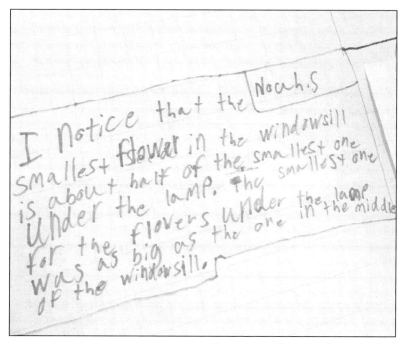

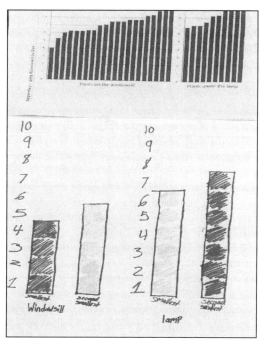

Figure 8a. Comparing one bar to another.

Some students will focus on the range, noting that the windowsill group ranges from 4 to 9½—a difference of 5½ inches. In contrast, the plants grown under the lamp have a much tighter spread, ranging from 6½ to 9½—a difference of only 3 inches. As a way to answer the second question students may find midpoints of the ranges and compare them for an answer of 1¼ inches. Note how Stella and Amelia also notice how "the middle of the ones under the lamp is bigger than 16 of the ones on the windowsill. And the shortest one under the lamp is the same as the middle under the windowsill." See Figure 8b.

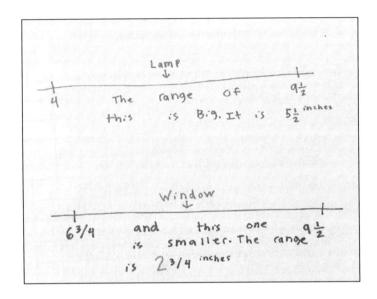
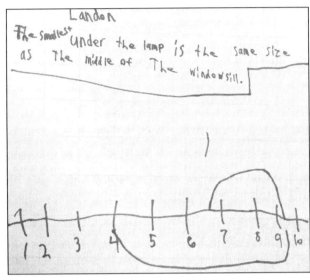

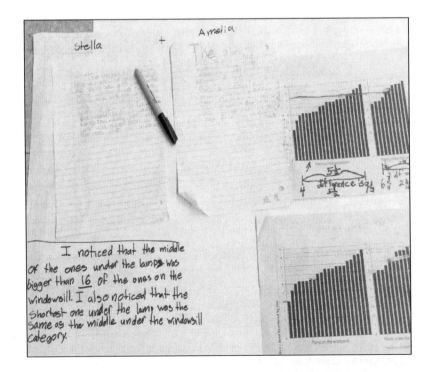
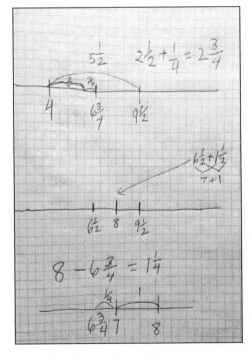

Figure 8b. Examining the range

Still other students will examine the central tendencies, the midpoints (medians), the clusters, and the shape of the data noting that the plants grown under the lamp all fit in the upper half of the graph of the plants grown on the windowsill. This is a particularly nice strategy and should be encouraged. See Figure 8c.

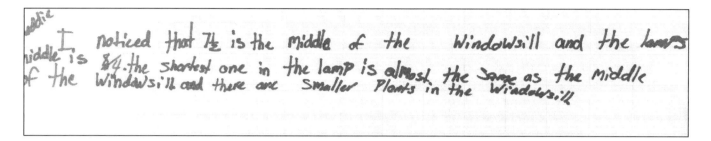

Figure 8c. Examining the Midpoints.

All of these approaches are fine, however. This investigation is meant as an exploratory investigation that engages students in examining central tendencies and variation in an intuitive, informal way. It is not intended to formally teach descriptive statistics and procedures to derive them. When students have had enough time to examine and discuss the results, move them into journal writing so they have an opportunity to reflect on the conclusions they have drawn from the evidence of the results of the experiment. Tomorrow they will begin by reading over their notes and making a poster of their conclusions and justifications. A gallery walk and congress will follow.

Reflections on the Day

Math workshop began today with a minilesson designed to encourage students to make use of number relations when analyzing and comparing data on a bar graph. As students moved into the investigation of analyzing and comparing two sets of data, they engaged in examining central tendencies, the range of the data, and the idea of the median likely arose naturally in the discussion. As they worked to explore the difference from the shortest to tallest plants in the two collections, they were working on a grade 4 CCSS end of year outcome. Are your students able to show competency already on this end-of-year outcome, or will you need to support them further?

DAY SEVEN

DATA ANALYSIS

Materials Needed

Student Work from Day Six (and copies of the related appendices as needed)

Chart paper

Scissors

Markers

Glue sticks

Pencils and Math Journals

Sticky notes

Today begins with students looking back over the notes they made in their math journals on Day Six and discussing their work and the notes with their math partner. Then the pair makes a poster of the conclusions they have drawn from the evidence of the results of the experiment, with particular emphasis placed on using the data for justifications. A gallery walk and congress follow.

Day Seven Outline

Preparing for a Gallery Walk

❖ Have students review their notes from Day Six and begin making a poster of their conclusions and justifications.

❖ Move around and confer with a few pairs as they work and then have all students display their posters around the room.

❖ Pass out sticky notes and have students review classmates' posters.

Facilitating the Math Congress

❖ Choose two or three posters for a focused discussion on ways to interpret the data from the two conditions.

❖ Examine and promote discussion specifically on what conclusions can be drawn from the data and how graphs can be used for interpretation and analysis of the data.

Preparing for the Gallery Walk

Have students meet with their partners from the prior day to review their work and to discuss the notes they took in their math journals as they reflected on conclusions and justifications regarding the experiment on plant conditions. As students work, listen in on their discussions and note how they are dealing with the two questions:

❖ Did the plants under the lamp, with 24 hours of light, grow more than the plants on the windowsill?

❖ If they did, how many inches more did they grow?

Invite students to use chart paper to make posters for a gallery walk and provide them with chart paper and markers. Then move around and confer with a few pairs as they work. As you confer, note the different strategies students are using and start thinking about which posters might be good ones to use in the congress.

After a sufficient amount of time, have students display their posters around the room and provide sticky notes for review comments. If students finish at different times, and not all are

> **Teacher Note**
>
> It is helpful if you review the Overview section of the unit to help you spot big ideas as they arise. It may also be helpful to look back over the Day Six discussion of possible strategies on pages 43-45.

ready at the same time, don't be concerned. Explain that mathematicians often aren't done when they ask another mathematician for feedback. Reviewers can think about what they would do next on the poster and make suggestions and this can be very helpful even if the poster is not yet finished.

Facilitating the Math Congress

Choose two or three posters to use for a focused discussion on analysis of the data. Invite students to the meeting area and convene a congress. If you have a pair that has used a 1-1 correspondence strategy—comparing bars to bars (for example noting that the tallest windowsill plant is about the same as the tallest plant under the lamp, but that the shortest plants in each group are quite different and the shortest plant is in the windowsill group), this might be a good group to start with, particularly if they have also looked at midpoint bars. This is a nice place to define median as it emerges naturally. The median of the windowsill group (plant #11) is about 7½ inches; whereas the two "middle plants" (#5 and #6) in the plants under the lamp are about 8¼ inches. A second poster should discuss the range. Others can be used also if you think they will add to the discussion. The main focus of the congress should be how graphs can be analyzed so the data across conditions can be compared and that one of the ways to do that is to look for clusters, the range, and the central tendency. A window into one classroom during a congress follows as an example:

Jennifer (the teacher): Let's start the congress with this poster. This is yours, Alena and Maia, right? Would you start us off?

Maia: Both had tall plants, and the tallest ones were even the same. That surprised us! The short ones were different though. This one (*pointing to the plants grown on the windowsill)* has a really short one. It is only 4 inches. Under the lamp, the shortest plant is 6¾ inches.

Alena: Right. And then we noticed that *all* the ones under the lamp sort of fit right over the tallest ones on the windowsill. See. Ten here and ten there. They are sort of the same.

Salena: 10, no 11, is the middle of that one. That's why.

Jennifer: Is that what you mean Alena?

Alena: Well, sort of, but not really. I mean, it is about half, but also most of the short ones are in the other half. See? *(She points to the half on the left.)* These are all short.

Jennifer: That's an interesting way of looking at the two graphs, isn't it? Where is the exact halfway point on the graph of the plants grown on the windowsill?

Maia: It's the 11th bar, because there are 10 on this side of it, and 10 on the other side. So, this one is right in the middle and it is 7½ inches. And see, it's like the 10 grown under the lamp fit with the 10 here and they are the biggest. Well, sort of. There's a few from under the lamp that are a little shorter than 7½. But, look at all the other short ones!

Alena: I just noticed something, too. If you find the middle one of the ones under the lamp, it's 8¼. That's a lot bigger.

Jennifer: Stella, what are you thinking about? You look puzzled.

Stella: Well Amelia and I found the middle, too. But our way was different, and we got different numbers. The windowsill plants went from 4 to 9½. And the plants under the lamp went from 6½ to 9½.

Jennifer: Come show your poster, Stella, so everyone can see what you are talking about.

Stella: See. We got 6¾ inches and 8 inches as the middles.

Author's notes

Jennifer starts with Maia and Alena hoping to support a conversation on the median.

She notices her moment emerging and she uses it to focus attention on the midpoint of each data set.

Now both medians can be compared.

By inviting Stella to share, the midpoint of the range can be compared to the midpoint of the data set. Both the range and the median are now the focus.

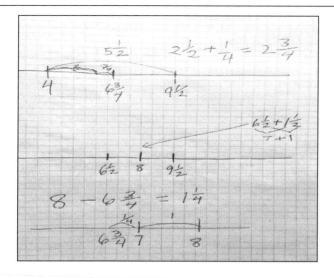

Jennifer: Everyone turn and talk to a partner. What's the middle? Middle of what? Why do Stella and Amelia have different numbers than Alena and Maia? *(During the pair talk, Jennifer listens in and moves around. After a sufficient amount of time she resumes whole group discussion.)* Salena, what did you and Jada talk about?

Salena: We think they are different middles. Maia and Alena mean the middle of the bars, not the middle of the... what do you call that?

Jennifer: The range?

Salena: Yeah, the range. You *(looking at Stella)* did the midpoint of the distance between 6½ and 9½. You found the midpoint of the difference from the shortest to the tallest. Maia and Alena are talking about the middle bar. Over there, there are 21 bars, so #11 is the one in the middle. There are 10 bars on each side of it. With the ones under the lamp, there are only 10 bars, so the middle is like...between #5 and #6. There's 5 on each side.

Stella: Oh, I get it! We are both right. It's just another way of looking at it!

Jennifer: Yes. You found the midpoints of the ranges, and Maia and Alena found something that mathematicians call the median. And can both of these ways help us answer the question of whether the plants under the lamp grew more?

Max: Yes. The plants under the lamp grew more. You can just see it in the graphs. All the ones under the lamp fit in the upper half of the ones on the windowsill.

Pair talk is critical here and Jennifer uses it to keep everyone focused.

The difference between the two strategies is now the focus and the terms range and median have both been introduced as a natural part of the discussion. Jennifer now invites consideration of what Max has noticed as he focused on examining the midpoint.

Reflections on the Day

Data analysis was the focus of the work today. Students are not only learning how to graph; they are learning to analyze data sets and to compare them using graphs. Doing so is an important skill in the 21st century where we are presented everyday with data. Years ago, the basic skill was arithmetic–to be able to calculate. Today, computers do most of the calculating and we are expected to analyze the output. To function wisely, and live our lives competently, we need to be able to represent quantitative relationships using a variety of representations and we need to have multiple ways of structuring data sets and analyzing them. Today your young mathematicians engaged in developing a qualitative notion of a distribution of data as an object with certain characteristics, such as shape and spread. They were learning to compare these objects, describe the differences, and even make conclusions about the effects of light on the growth of plants. Now is a good time to relook at the landscape and to review the Overview section of the unit. Where is each student on the landscape?

DAY EIGHT

THE HEIGHTS OF NBA PLAYERS

Materials Needed

Meter stick with feet and inches marked on the other side

Estimates of Heights on an NBA Team (Appendix K, one per student)

Heights of All NBA Players in One Year (Appendix K, one per student)

Focus Questions on NBA Heights (Appendix M, one per student)

Rulers

Chart paper

Markers

Today students predict the heights of NBA basketball players and make a line plot of the heights of what they think might be a typical team of 15 male players. They are then presented with a line-plot showing the real data of 470 NBA players on the men's teams. They compare the two line-plots noting whether they were close or not and analyze the real data to draw conclusions about the heights of NBA players on the men's teams.

Day Eight Outline

Developing the Context

❖ Show images of a few well-known basketball players and then support a discussion on what they think the heights of players on a typical men's team might be.

❖ Build a line plot together of what might be the heights of a typical team until consensus is reached.

❖ Then send students off to build a line plot of their own for an imagined typical team, which they should also name.

Supporting the Investigation

❖ Move around and confer, supporting students to build a line plot of a team of their own.

❖ When students have completed a line plot of their own teams, distribute a table of real data for comparison (Appendix L) and ask them to compare the two graphs.

❖ Provide time for making posters of their conclusions.

❖ Bring students together for a discussion on their findings.

Developing the Context

Start a discussion on the heights of basketball players and why it might help to be tall if one is a basketball player. If you do an internet search for *heights of basketball players* you will find lots of images that you can use to develop the context, but don't show any charts, just a few images of some players they might know to get them interested in the context. Ask students what they think the range of height is for NBA players. Ask what they think the most common height (the mode) is. Use a meter stick with the feet and inches marked on the other side and measure out some of the heights to help them imagine how high that is. Discuss the lengths in both feet and meters and centimeters. Students don't need to be able to formally convert from one system to another at this point in their development, but it is nice to build an informal, intuitive sense of the magnitude of the lengths in both systems. Using a meter stick with the feet and inches marked on the other side helps them begin to see that a meter is about 40 inches, so a meter is about 4 inches (or 10 centimeters) more than a yard (or 3 feet).

Share that there are up to 15 players signed on an NBA basketball team. Only 12 can be dressed and ready to play in games, however. For 15 players, ask what they think the heights might be and build a line plot with them that they think might be reflective of the heights of a typical team. Allow discussion and revision until a line plot is made that there is general consensus on. When you are done it will likely look something like this:

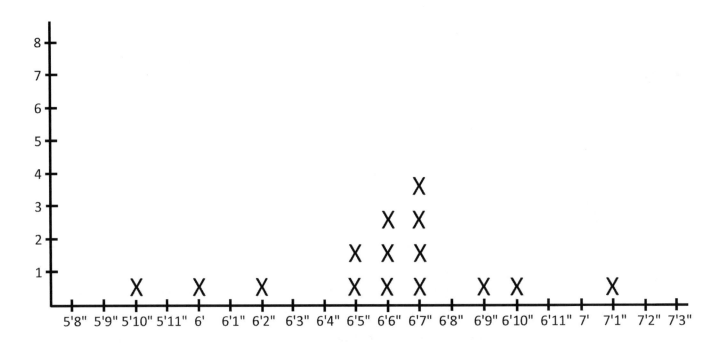

Figure 9. Line plot of an imagined typical team.

Send students off to make a line plot of their own imagined typical team with copies of Appendix K.

Supporting the Investigation

As students work, move around and listen in to the conversations.

The reason for not providing graph paper is so you can see if students align the Xs. If not, confer with them on why it is important to do so if one wants to be able to compare the heights of the stacks without counting. Suggest they make lines with rulers.

As they finish, distribute Appendix L, a bar graph showing the data on all 470 NBA players in a year[2]. Ask them to compare the real data to the imagined team they made. Were their guesses close, or way off? Were there any surprises for them in the real data? Make clear that you cannot predict a specific team from overall data. Do not give the impression that the better a graph resembles the overall data, the better it is. A specific team may have more short players and still be very successful. So, in a sense, any guess is as good as that of someone else. But students love making up an imagined team and when they see the real data they are often surprised. The point of this activity is just to hook the children into the context and to create the element of surprise.

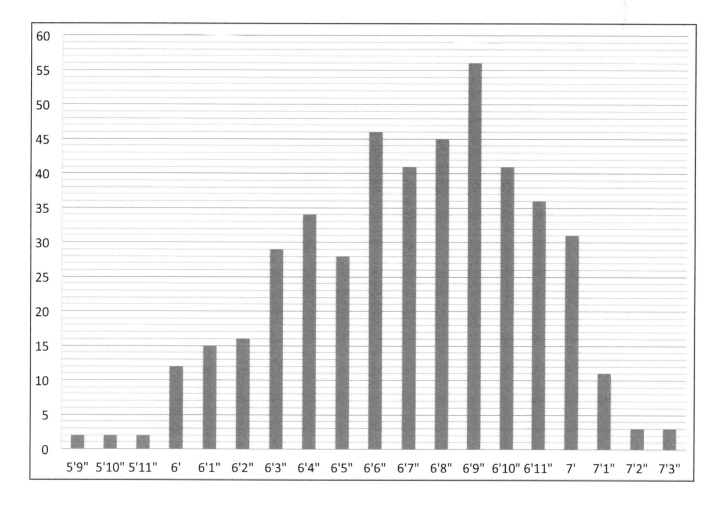

[2] data from NBA's stats page

- ❖ Do the overall shapes of the graphs look similar? If so how, if not, how are they different?
- ❖ What is the range of the line plot on their team? What is the difference in height from the shortest to the tallest? What is the range and the difference in height from the shortest to the tallest in the real data?
- ❖ Are the modes (the most common height) on both line plots the same? If not, how close were you? Are there clusters? Are they the same?
- ❖ Are the medians the same—the point in the middle where half the players are taller, and half the players are shorter? What is the median in your plot? Were you close to the real data?
- ❖ When you looked at the real data, what surprised you the most?

Provide each student with the list of focus questions (Appendix M) and have each student make a poster about their team compared to the real data. Display them around the room. Depending on time, you can have a gallery walk and then a congress. But if time does not allow, you may prefer to just have a gallery walk and then bring the class back for a brief discussion on the real data on Appendix L.

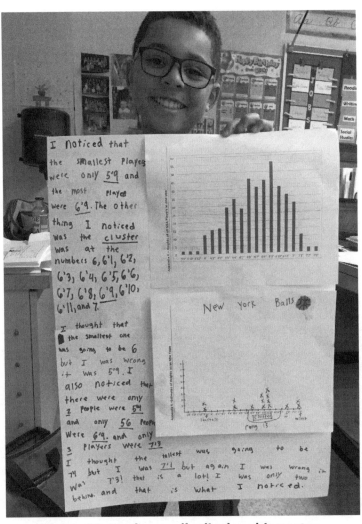

Figure 10: Noah proudly displays his poster.

Reflections on the Day

Today your students constructed a line plot of their predictions of the heights of a typical NBA men's team and compared their line plot with a bar graph of real data of the heights of all NBA male players in a given year. Throughout this unit they have been analyzing a variety of graphs and discussing conclusions that can be drawn from them. A nice homework or project assignment to continue the work of today is to have students find out the heights of players on their favorite team (male or female teams; it's all provided on the NBA team stats site). They can make a line plot for their favorite team and then compare that team to the fuller NBA data. Reports can be shared to the class.

DAY NINE

WHAT'S WRONG WITH THIS GRAPH?

Materials Needed

Growth of One Player (Appendix N, one per student)

Line Graph Template (Appendix O, one per student)

Focus Questions on a NBA Player's Growth (Appendix P, one per student)

Pencils

Math Journals

Today students learn about a basketball player who is 6½ feet tall (78 inches, which is almost two meters tall, and just one-inch shy of the median of all male NBA players). A table of his height through the years is shown as well as a line graph of the data. Discussion occurs on why the growth pattern on the graph looks wrong, and eventually the need for a scale that reflects equal intervals arises. Students work to redo the line graph and consider how the newer growth pattern compares and what can now be determined about the player's growth. Emphasis is placed on the difference between curved lines and straight lines on a line graph and what they mean.

Day Nine Outline

Developing the Context

❖ Tell students about a basketball player who is 6½ ft tall—almost 2 meters.

❖ Display a table of data of his height through the years and a line graph a reporter made to show his growth (Appendix N).

❖ Ask students to discuss what is wrong with the graph and then send them off to redo the line graph (Appendix O) and to examine the new growth patterns that occur and to explain why they look different on the two graphs.

Supporting the Investigation

❖ Move around and confer, supporting students to consider what is wrong with the first graph and how it might be corrected.

❖ Have students redo the graph onto Appendix O, work on the focus questions on Appendix P, and reflect in their journals.

Developing the Context

Explain to students that you have learned of a basketball player that was recently being interviewed by a journalist. He told the journalist that he was 6½ feet tall (78"), which is close to 2 meters tall, and just 1 inch shy of the median of all the NBA players on the men's teams. So he is pretty typical. He also told the journalist that he was always the tallest kid in the class. He had found some medical reports from his youth and he gave the journalist the data he had found. Display Appendix N (components shown below).

Years	Inches
0	21
2	36 ¾
4	44
8	55 ½
10	60 ¼
14	71 ¾
18	76 ½
20	78

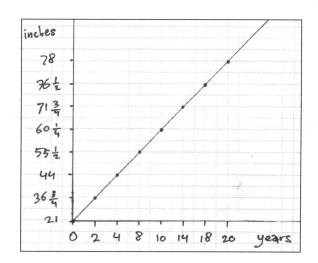

The journalist thought it would be interesting to add a graph of the data to the article he was writing—a graph of how the basketball player had grown through the years. Using the data from the table, he drew a graph, but then he immediately thought: "No, this cannot be right!"

Ask students the question: Why do you think the journalist thought something was wrong with this graph? Provide five minutes or so of pair talk and then invite whole group discussion. Focus the discussion on the form of the graph by encouraging students to consider:

❖ Could this be true? Can it be a straight line? Why not?
❖ It looks from the line that he is just going to continue growing. Don't we all stop growing taller at some point?
❖ It looks on the graph as if the speed of growth through the years has not changed. Is that true? Has the speed of his growth been constant? Or were there growth spurts like the sunflower? In fact, between the years of 18 and 20, the player only grew 1½ inches; whereas in the first two years of life he grew 15½ inches!
❖ What did the reporter do wrong that made his graph show such weird things?

Students at this point will likely start remembering the problems that occurred when they did the sunflower investigation and they will begin to talk about the need to include all intervals. When it is clear to everyone that the numbers along the height axis should be from 0 to 78, and the numbers along the time axis should be from 0 to 20, with all intervals evenly spaced, provide them with Appendix O and send them off to work with a partner, asking each student to plot the data on the graph individually.

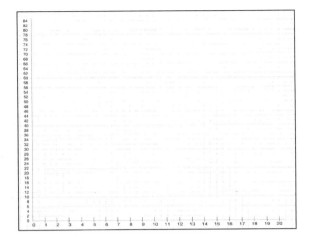

Move around and confer. If needed, help students to realize that the height scale goes up in increments of two inches. This means that several of the points, which are in half inches, will only be ¼ of the distance between the lines, as the halfway point would be the missing inch mark. In contrast, the time line along the bottom is marked in 1-year increments on the scale but there are lines between the numbers representing the half-year marks. Note how Appendix O has been carefully crafted to provide students with an opportunity to plot points on a *scaled* graph. They will need to think hard about the scales and work carefully to plot the points. For that reason, although each student will be plotting a graph, they are working in pairs so they can talk and help each other. Allow time and provide extra copies of Appendix O for revisions if needed. When they have finished graphing the data, all students should have the graph shown in Figure 11.

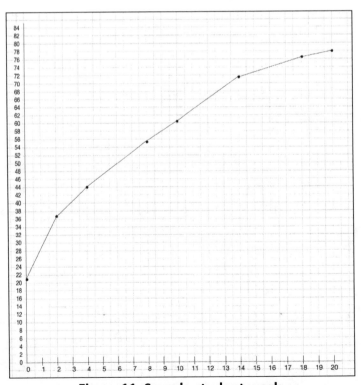

Figure 11. Sample student work.

When graphs are complete, bring students together for a brief discussion on the structure of the scales, the challenges of plotting the points, and the strategies they found helpful. Then form small groups (4-6 students in each). Appoint a facilitator and recorder of the discussion in each and provide each group with Appendix P (focus questions), blank chart paper, and a dark marker. Ask them to discuss the questions and record their thoughts. Then provide a 5-minute journal writing time for further independent reflection.

Appendix P – Focus Questions on NBA Player's Growth

❖ Why doesn't the line start at 0 years/0 inches?
❖ Has the basketball player stopped growing?
❖ Why is the line less steep when the growth is slower? What will the line look like when growth has stopped?

Reflections on the Day

Today the work centered on analyzing a line graph and noting the need for consistent intervals. As students redid the graphs they grappled with questions about how the axes were scaled, what the 0,0-point means, and how growth patterns can be observed and analyzed given the curve of the line. They compared straight lines to curved lines and explored how line graphs allow one to interpolate the points between the known values. This is some challenging math for fourth graders! It is however the math that students growing up in the 21st century should be focused on and the contexts, models, and discussions have supported them to construct it. Feel proud that by doing this type of mathematics you are developing learners who will be numerate enough to succeed in the years to come. If you have time tonight read their journals and respond back. When students know you are reading their entries thoughtfully and will engage in conversation back in a written form, they develop a seriousness about their entries and they look forward to your response. Lay the graphs out in front of you and document the growth you see from their early work in this unit on the sunflower's growth, to the work you see today. Take pictures of their work and the writing they did on the questions. Tomorrow will begin with a discussion on the work in a gallery walk and a congress, then a learning scroll will be made depicting the many things students learned as they progressed through the unit.

DAY TEN

REFLECTING ON DATA REPRESENTATION AND ANALYSIS

Materials Needed

Students' work from Day Nine

Extra copies of the appendices from Day Nine as needed

Students' work from throughout the unit

Pencils

Sticky Notes

Math Journals

Today students reconvene in the small groups of yesterday to briefly review the notes in their journals and add any needed finishing touches to their group posters. A gallery walk and math congress are then held with discussion focused on the questions on Appendix P. As a culmination to the unit, a learning scroll is made to represent and document the learning about data representation and analysis that occurred during the sequence of investigations in the unit.

Day Ten Outline

Facilitating the Gallery Walk
❖ Have students review the work they did on Day Nine and finish the posters they made of the discussion on the questions (Appendix P).
❖ Distribute sticky notes and begin a gallery walk.

Facilitating the Math Congress
❖ Choose a few groups to present their posters and share the issues they discussed as they worked on the questions.

Building a Learning Scroll
❖ With your students, reflect on the last two weeks as you progressed through this unit. Go through the work together and have students talk about some of the work they produced, the new ideas and strategies they learned and the realizations they had about different types of graphs, scales, and what they might show.

Facilitating the Gallery Walk

Provide students time to review their journal notes and finish their group posters begun on Day Nine. Then have them display their posters, distribute lined 3" by 5" sticky notes, and begin a gallery walk. As they work, think about which groups you want to use to support a conversation on the questions on Appendix P during the congress.

Look for posters that address some of the following big ideas:

❖ How aligning the scales with consistently spaced intervals and with a (0,0) point allows the scales to intersect and align in a way that the relationship of inches of height to time and the resulting growth patterns are noticeable.

❖ How does the shape of the line tell whether a player is still growing or is reaching the maximum height? How does the steepness of a line reflect growth?

❖ Can points on the line between the known data points be interpolated on a line graph? How?

Facilitating the Math Congress

This congress should not be a share of posters, nor a discussion on the answers to the questions. Students likely dealt with those discussions already as they worked. You'll want to structure it around the main points listed above. As students discuss the questions let the conversation flow into all the things they have learned over the progression of the unit. Pull out some of the work from prior days and have students talk about what they thought when they did that work and what they now know. Use this conversation to construct a learning scroll.

Building the Learning Scroll

A learning scroll is a class display—a sort of "socio-historical" wall documenting the progression of the learning, children's questions, and the important ideas constructed over the past two weeks. You'll want to include samples of students' work, descriptions of their strategies and ideas, and anecdotes of how students' thinking changed over time. The scroll is meant to be a document of the progression and emergence of learning over the past two weeks. By making this display available, you allow your students to revisit and reflect on all the wonderful ideas and strategies that emerged as they worked throughout the unit. Developmentally, even fourth graders will need you to scaffold some of this reflection work, but they will also be able to partner in identifying and describing their thoughts and strategies.

In preparation for today's work, use a roll of chart paper and cut out a long length sufficient to cover a bulletin board or a display area in a hallway. Curl and staple the two ends, making a small roll on each end. Staple or tape the scroll to the area to be covered. Make copies or take pictures of samples of some of the work your students produced on each day, reduced so that you can fit the work on the scroll. On the left begin with the graphs that students made of the growth of the sunflower. Pick a few samples where the intervals were not shown and how the line showing growth was straight. Make a conversation bubble and add a picture of the student saying, "We only graphed the data on the table and we got a straight line! Then we realized it would be better to show all the intervals!" Next to it display a picture of a graph that did show the intervals. Selectively pick other key pieces of children's work from the ten days of the unit and include these on a pathway from left to right, leaving plenty of blank space for anecdotes and explanations. You can also include pictures of the students and use speech bubbles to show insights they had along the way, or even ideas they may have had that were eventually disproved. End with some of the line plots from days nine and ten, with some descriptions of things your students said from analyzing the shape of the data.

You may want to provide templates with empty speech bubbles with prompts like "At first I thought…" "Then I realized…" and "A good strategy was…" Attach these student explanations to the learning scroll. Wherever you can, show the developmental emergence of ideas on the landscape in the Overview. Display the scroll in a place where your students, and hopefully also the wider school community, can revisit and reflect on the learning that happened.

Reflections on the Unit

> *"Instructional programs from prekindergarten through grade 12 should enable all students to create and use representations to organize, record, and communicate mathematical ideas; select, apply, and translate among mathematical representations to solve problems; [and] use representations to model and interpret physical, social, and mathematical phenomena."*
>
> National Council of Teachers of Mathematics, 2000, p. 67

Over the course of this unit, your students have been immersed in representing and analyzing data. The activities have supported them to understand what the displays mean and even to use them to compare the effects of sunlight on plant growth. Yesterday and today you witnessed more of their growing understanding of data and representation as they analyzed the shape and variance of the data, what it meant, and how they could use it to compare the results of the heights of basketball players.

This is a good time now to step back and reflect on the landscape. Look at the learning scroll that you and your students made as you reflected on the last two weeks. What movement along the landscape have you seen? Document the growth you see evidence of on the scroll. Put it on each student's landscape!

Appendix A – A Sunflower Picture

Weeks of Growth	Length in cm
4	17
5	36
9	169
14	253
15	254

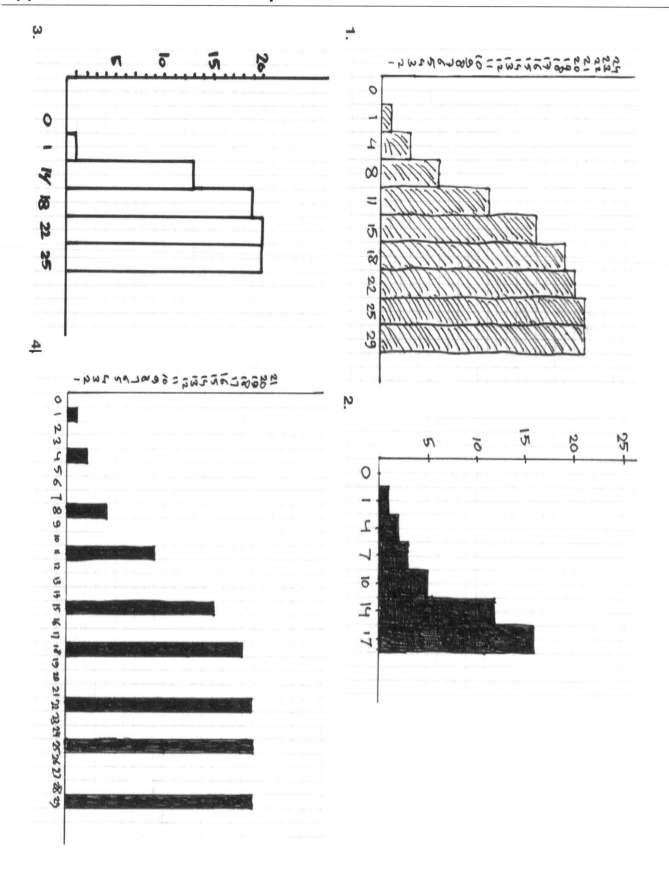

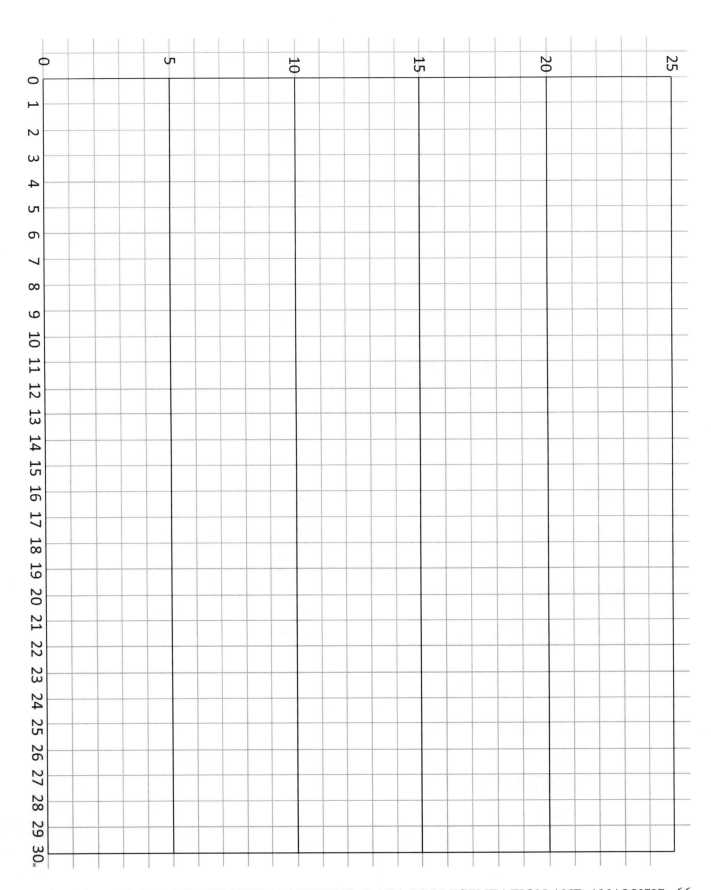

❖ Are there differences in the growth patterns of the four plants?

❖ What can you tell in general about the growth of this kind of plant?

❖ About how high do the plants become?

❖ Do the plants all grow at the same speed all the time, or do they have growth spurts like the sunflower where they grow quickly?

❖ About how long does it take for a Brassica Rapa plant to reach its full height?

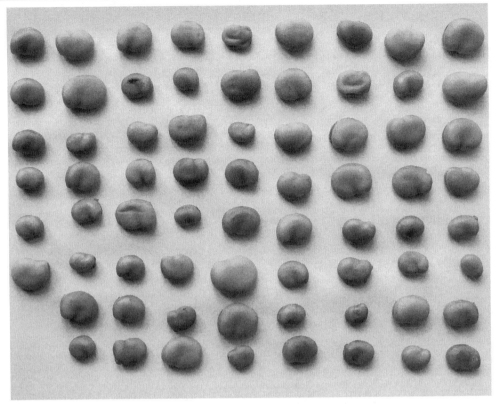

Beans grown without fertilizer

Beans grown with fertilizer

Appendix G – Measurement Data on Beans from Different Soil Conditions

$\frac{5}{8}$	$\frac{3}{4}$	$\frac{5}{8}$	$\frac{5}{8}$	$\frac{1}{2}$	$\frac{3}{4}$	$\frac{5}{8}$	$\frac{3}{4}$	$\frac{3}{4}$
$\frac{5}{8}$	$\frac{7}{8}$	$\frac{5}{8}$	$\frac{1}{2}$	$\frac{3}{4}$	$\frac{5}{8}$	$\frac{5}{8}$	$\frac{1}{2}$	$\frac{7}{8}$
$\frac{5}{8}$	$\frac{1}{2}$	$\frac{5}{8}$	$\frac{3}{4}$	$\frac{1}{2}$	$\frac{3}{4}$	$\frac{3}{4}$	$\frac{3}{4}$	$\frac{3}{4}$
$\frac{1}{2}$	$\frac{5}{8}$	$\frac{5}{8}$	$\frac{5}{8}$	$\frac{5}{8}$	$\frac{5}{8}$	$\frac{3}{4}$	$\frac{3}{4}$	$\frac{5}{8}$
$\frac{1}{2}$	$\frac{5}{8}$	$\frac{3}{4}$	$\frac{1}{2}$	$\frac{3}{4}$	$\frac{5}{8}$	$\frac{5}{8}$	$\frac{1}{2}$	$\frac{5}{8}$
$\frac{3}{4}$	$\frac{1}{2}$	$\frac{1}{2}$	$\frac{5}{8}$	$\frac{7}{8}$	$\frac{5}{8}$	$\frac{5}{8}$	$\frac{1}{2}$	$\frac{3}{8}$
	$\frac{3}{4}$	$\frac{5}{8}$	$\frac{1}{2}$	$\frac{3}{4}$	$\frac{1}{2}$	$\frac{3}{8}$	$\frac{5}{8}$	$\frac{5}{8}$
	$\frac{1}{2}$	$\frac{5}{8}$	$\frac{3}{4}$	$\frac{1}{2}$	$\frac{5}{8}$	$\frac{1}{2}$	$\frac{1}{2}$	$\frac{5}{8}$

Beans grown
without fertilizer

$\frac{7}{8}$	$\frac{5}{8}$	$\frac{3}{4}$	$\frac{3}{4}$	$\frac{3}{4}$	$\frac{3}{4}$	1	$\frac{1}{2}$	$\frac{7}{8}$
$\frac{5}{8}$	$\frac{1}{2}$	$\frac{3}{4}$	$\frac{5}{8}$	$\frac{3}{4}$	$\frac{5}{8}$	$\frac{1}{2}$	$\frac{3}{4}$	$\frac{7}{8}$
$\frac{3}{4}$	$\frac{5}{8}$	$\frac{3}{4}$	$\frac{7}{8}$	$\frac{3}{4}$	$\frac{3}{4}$	$\frac{7}{8}$	$\frac{3}{4}$	$\frac{3}{4}$
1	$\frac{3}{4}$	$\frac{3}{4}$	$\frac{1}{2}$	$\frac{3}{4}$	$\frac{5}{8}$	$\frac{3}{4}$	$\frac{7}{8}$	$\frac{7}{8}$
	$\frac{3}{4}$	$\frac{3}{4}$	$\frac{5}{8}$	$\frac{5}{8}$	$\frac{5}{8}$	$\frac{7}{8}$	$\frac{3}{4}$	$\frac{3}{4}$
	$\frac{3}{4}$	$\frac{7}{8}$	$\frac{1}{2}$	$\frac{3}{4}$	$\frac{5}{8}$	$\frac{7}{8}$	$\frac{3}{4}$	$\frac{3}{4}$
	$\frac{3}{4}$	$\frac{3}{4}$	$\frac{3}{4}$	$\frac{3}{4}$	$\frac{1}{2}$	$\frac{3}{4}$	$\frac{7}{8}$	$1\frac{1}{8}$
	$\frac{3}{4}$	$\frac{5}{8}$	$\frac{3}{4}$	$\frac{3}{4}$	$\frac{5}{8}$	$\frac{3}{4}$	$\frac{3}{4}$	1

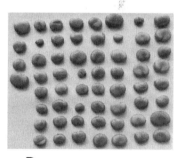

Beans grown
with fertilizer

Appendix H – Lengths of Growing Seasons

Data is from https://www.dummies.com/home-garden/gardening/growing-seasons-by-hardiness-zone/

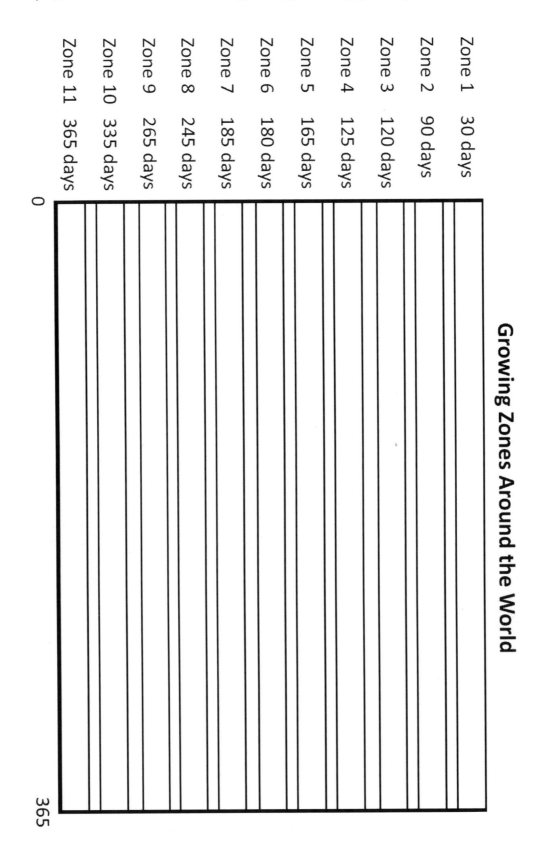

Zone 1   30 days
Zone 2   90 days
Zone 3   120 days
Zone 4   125 days
Zone 5   165 days
Zone 6   180 days
Zone 7   185 days
Zone 8   245 days
Zone 9   265 days
Zone 10   335 days
Zone 11   365 days

Growing Zones Around the World

Appendix I – Data from Plant Experiment

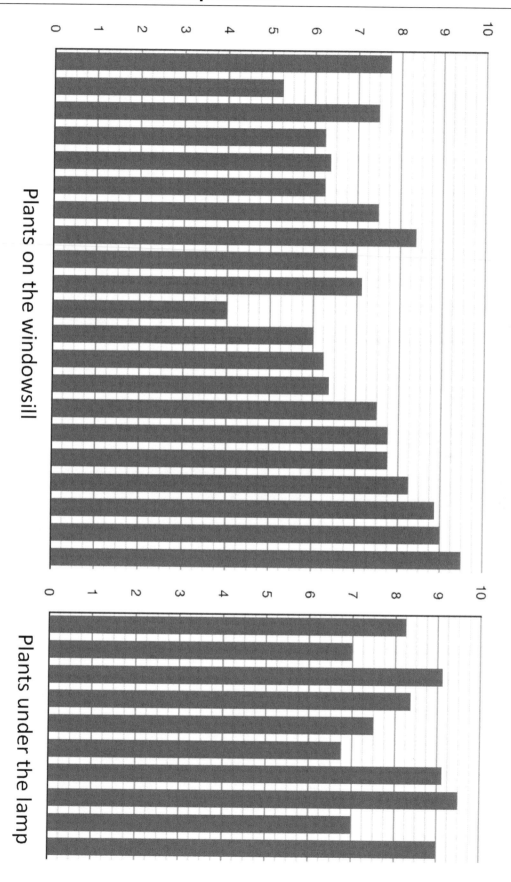

Appendix J – Data Reordered by Size

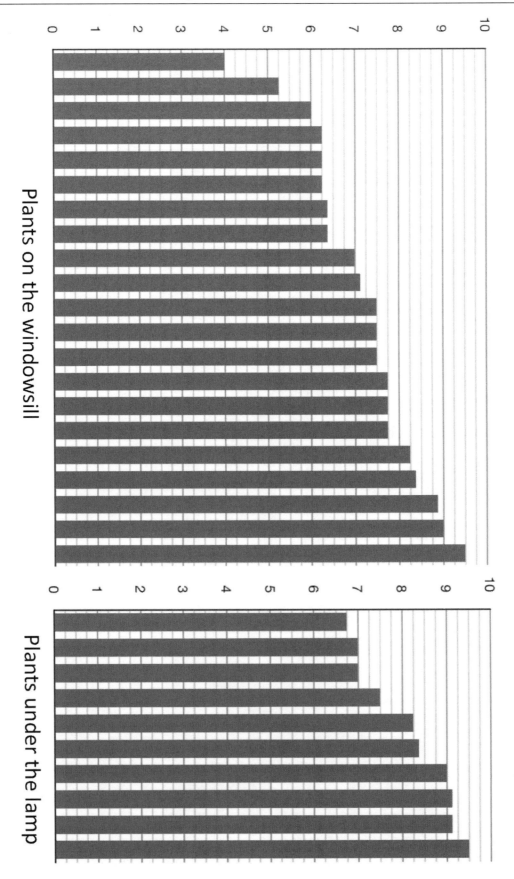

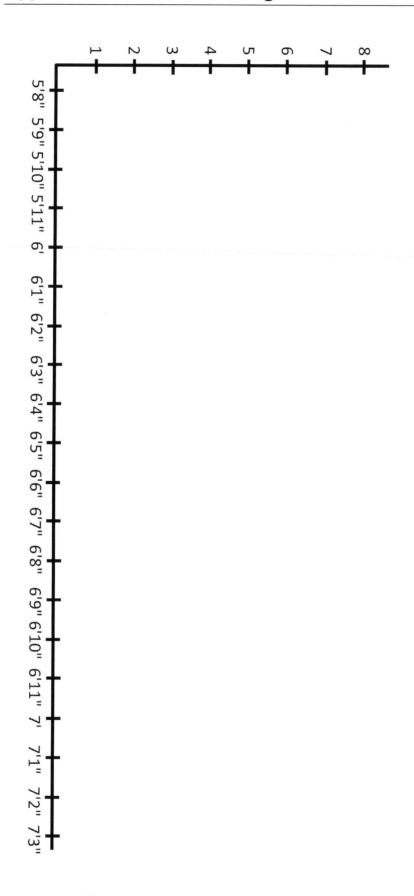

Appendix L - Heights of all NBA Players in One Year

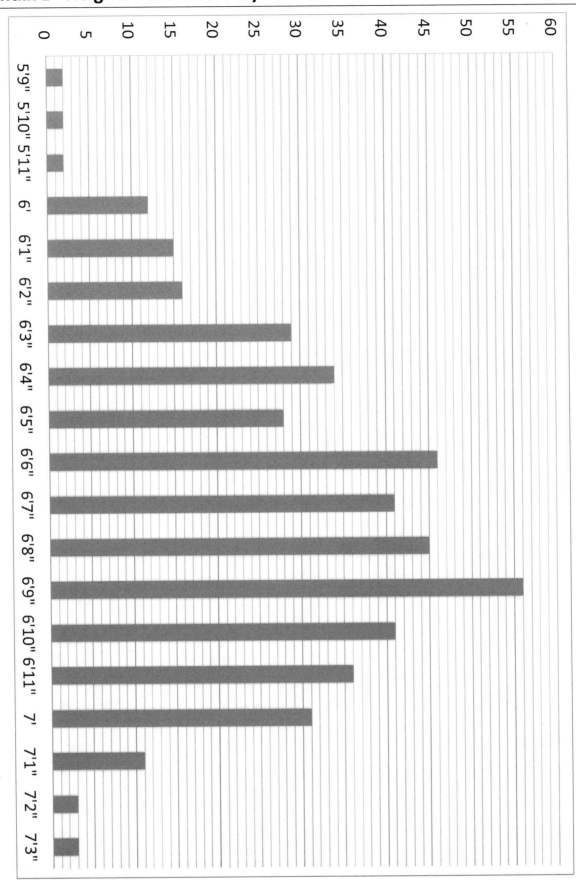

❖ Do the overall shapes of the graphs look similar? If so, how? If not, how are they different?

❖ What is the range of the line plot we came up with?

On ours, what is the difference in height from the shortest to the tallest?

What is the range and the difference in height from the shortest to the tallest in the real data?

❖ Are the modes (the most common height) on both line plots the same? If not, how close were we? Are there clusters? Are they similar?

❖ Are the medians the same—the point in the middle where half the players are taller, and half the players are shorter? What is the median in our plot? Were we close?

❖ When you looked at the real data, what surprised you the most?

Years	Inches
0	21
2	36 ¾
4	44
8	55 ½
10	60 ¼
14	71 ¾
18	76 ½
20	78

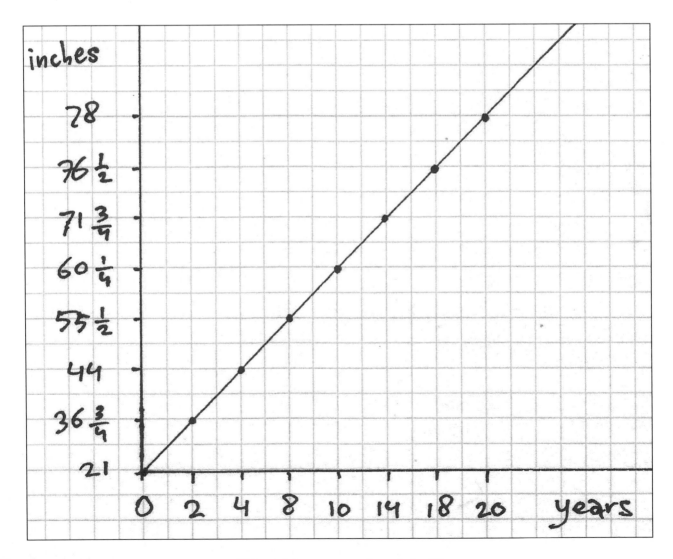

"No, this cannot be right!"

Appendix O – Line Graph Template

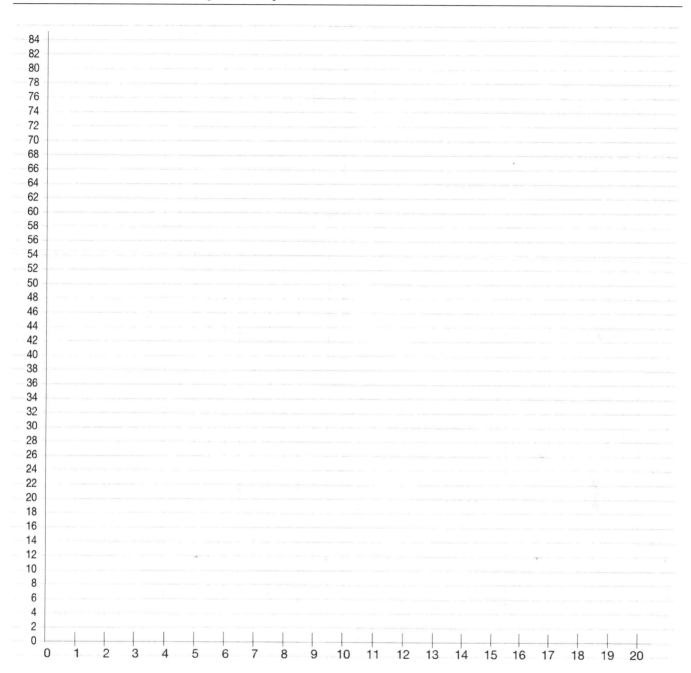

❖ Why doesn't the line start at 0 years/0 inches?

❖ Has the basketball player stopped growing?

❖ Why is the line less steep when the growth is slower? What will the line look like when growth has stopped?

Made in the USA
Monee, IL
23 January 2024